LOSE WEIGH

Slim·Fast! ®
③·②·① *Plan*

pil
Publications International, Ltd.

Front cover photography and photography on pages 42, 45, 47, 49, 51, 53, 64, 67, 69, 71, 90, 93, 95, 97, 118, 121, 122, 124, 126 and 128 by PIL Photo Studio, Chicago.
Pictured on the front cover: Eggplant "Lasagna" (*page 94*).
Pictured on the back cover: Mushroom, Onion & Pepper Smothered Burgers (*page 105*), Farfalle with Tuna, Lemon & Spinach (*page 100*) and Asian Salmon Salad (*page 92*).

ISBN-13: 978-1-4508-2274-9
ISBN-10: 1-4508-2274-6

Library of Congress Control Number: 2011921748

Manufactured in China.

8 7 6 5 4 3 2 1

Microwave Cooking: Microwave ovens vary in wattage. Use the cooking times as guidelines, and check for doneness before adding more time.

Nutritional Analysis: Every effort has been made to check the accuracy of the nutritional information that appears with each recipe. However, because numerous variables account for a wide range of values for certain foods, nutritive analyses in this book should be considered approximate. Different results may be obtained by using different nutrient databases and different brand-name products.

Preparation/Cooking Times: Preparation times are based on the approximate amount of time required to assemble the recipe before cooking, baking, chilling or serving. These times include preparation steps such as measuring, chopping and mixing. The fact that some preparations and cooking can be done simultaneously is taken into account. Preparation of optional ingredients and serving suggestions is not included.

Publications International, Ltd.

Contents

Slim·Fast!®
③ · ② · ① Plan

Want to slim down for a special occasion, and don't have time to waste? The **Slim·Fast® 3•2•1 Plan** gives you quick results*—done right. Plus, it's flexible, so you can get the structure you want with the variety you crave.

*Losing more than 2 lbs. per week is not recommended. Follow the Slim·Fast® 3•2•1 Plan and include regular exercise.

Just follow the plan:

SNACKS

Pick 3 nourishing snacks a day—Slim·Fast 100-calorie snack bars, nuts, fruits, and/or veggies. Snacking can be a good thing! In fact, it's an important part of the Slim·Fast 3•2•1 Plan. It keeps your metabolism going and gives you the energy you need to help get through the day.

SHAKES & MEAL BARS

Choose 2 Slim·Fast shakes or meal bars. Giving breakfast a break, leaving lunch behind, or taking a break from dinner is easier when you replace a meal with your choice of Slim·Fast shakes and meal bars in a range of delicious flavors.

BALANCED MEAL

Enjoy 1 (500-calorie) balanced meal per day. Our recipes are specifically designed by our Test Kitchens to provide delicious-tasting, 500-calorie meals that you can enjoy at home.

Slim·Fast!®
3·2·1 Plan

A balanced meal on the **Slim-Fast 3•2•1 Plan** is approximately 500 calories, and should include protein, starch, and vegetables to give you the nutritional balance that you need. As a general rule, try to fill ½ of your plate with vegetables, ¼ of your plate with lean protein (i.e. chicken, fish, turkey, or lean beef), and ¼ with starch (preferably whole grain).

Using this cookbook, you can create your balanced meal by combining recipes from the protein, starch, and vegetable chapters. We also offer a chapter on One-Dish Meals that will incorporate all the elements of the balanced meal in one recipe.

The snack chapter at the end of the cookbook provides options that you can use for your three snacks each day. These snacks are approximately 100 calories, so they can be interchanged with snacks such as Slim-Fast snack bars, fruits, vegetables, nonfat yogurt, low-fat cheese, and other 100-calorie food items.

Vegetable

lettuce
carrots
broccoli
cauliflower
peppers
green beans
asparagus
cabbage
eggplant
spinach

Protein

chicken
fish
beef
eggs
tofu
beans
pork

Starch

brown rice
potatoes
bread
yams
corn
peas
pasta

Slim·Fast! ®
3·2·1 *Plan*

Just follow the plan to lose weight, fast. Don't like one of the suggested snacks or balanced meals? Swap it for one you do. Just be sure the approximate calorie values are the same.

Week One

	Day One	**Day Two**	**Day Three**
2 SHAKES OR MEAL BARS **BREAKFAST**	Slim-Fast Shake or Meal Bar	Slim-Fast Shake or Meal Bar	Slim-Fast Shake or Meal Bar
3 SNACKS **SNACK**	1 cup diced pineapple	Apple Tea Latte (pg 122)	1 cup unsweetened applesauce
2 SHAKES OR MEAL BARS **LUNCH**	Slim-Fast Shake or Meal Bar	Slim-Fast Shake or Meal Bar	Slim-Fast Shake or Meal Bar
3 SNACKS **SNACK**	Slim-Fast Snack Bar	1 Tbsp. peanut butter on 2 (5-inch) celery stalks	Fruit Kabobs with Raspberry Yogurt Dip (pg 129)
1 BALANCED MEAL **DINNER**	Chicken Chipotle Stew (pg 106)	Honey Mustard Chicken Fingers (pg 24), Sweet 'N Nutty Orzo (pg 44), Italian Steamed Broccoli (pg 78)	Onion-Apple Glazed Pork Tenderloin (pg 27), Spicy Sweet Potato Rounds (pg 62), Honey Dijon Spinach Salad (pg 86)
3 SNACKS **SNACK**	Apple Streusel Muffins (pg 120)	Slim-Fast Snack Bar	Slim-Fast Snack Bar

3 snacks, 2 Slim-Fast shakes or meal bars, 1 balanced meal

Day Four	Day Five	Day Six	Day Seven
Slim-Fast Shake or Meal Bar	Slim-Fast Shake or Meal Bar	Slim-Fast Shake or Meal Bar	Slim-Fast Shake or Meal Bar
1 small banana	Slim-Fast Snack Bar	Trail Mix Truffles (pg 128)	2 tangerines
Slim-Fast Shake or Meal Bar	Slim-Fast Shake or Meal Bar	Slim-Fast Shake or Meal Bar	Slim-Fast Shake or Meal Bar
Slim-Fast Snack Bar	Banana & Chocolate Chip Pops (pg 130)	2 cups strawberries	Slim-Fast Snack Bar
Shrimp Marinara (pg 22), Veggie Brown Rice & Orzo Pilaf (pg 63), Baked Stuffed Zucchini (pg 65)	Black Bean Wraps (pg 114)	Pasta Caponata with Pork (pg 91)	1-2-3 Chicken Cacciatore (pg 26), Savory Skillet Potatoes (pg 60), Vegetable Medley Sauté (pg 76)
Berry Parfait (pg 139)	12 dried apricot halves	Slim-Fast Snack Bar	Carrot Cake Cookies (pg 138)

Just follow the plan to lose weight, fast. Don't like one of the suggested snacks or balanced meals?
Swap it for one you do. Just be sure the approximate calorie values are the same.

Week Two

	Day Eight	Day Nine	Day Ten
2 SHAKES OR MEAL BARS / **BREAKFAST**	Slim-Fast Shake or Meal Bar	Slim-Fast Shake or Meal Bar	Slim-Fast Shake or Meal Bar
3 SNACKS / **SNACK**	Zucchini Cake Snax (pg 137)	2 cups diced watermelon	1 cup cherries
2 SHAKES OR MEAL BARS / **LUNCH**	Slim-Fast Shake or Meal Bar	Slim-Fast Shake or Meal Bar	Slim-Fast Shake or Meal Bar
3 SNACKS / **SNACK**	Slim-Fast Snack Bar	Rosemary-Scented Nut Mix (pg 131)	Slim-Fast Snack Bar
1 BALANCED MEAL / **DINNER**	Warm White Bean & Tuna Quesadillas (pg 111)	Souperior Meat Loaf with Bell Peppers (pg 20), Herb-Crusted Russet Potatoes (pg 59), Grilled Green Beans (pg 79)	Skillet Turkey Caesar (pg 117)
3 SNACKS / **SNACK**	½ cup frozen yogurt	Slim-Fast Snack Bar	Strawberry Mango Popsicles (pg 126)

3 snacks, 2 Slim-Fast shakes or meal bars, 1 balanced meal

Day Eleven	Day Twelve	Day Thirteen	Day Fourteen
Slim-Fast Shake or Meal Bar	Slim-Fast Shake or Meal Bar	Slim-Fast Shake or Meal Bar	Slim-Fast Shake or Meal Bar
1 cup green grapes	1 cup diced pineapple	1½ cups fresh raspberries	Slim-Fast Snack Bar
Slim-Fast Shake or Meal Bar	Slim-Fast Shake or Meal Bar	Slim-Fast Shake or Meal Bar	Slim-Fast Shake or Meal Bar
30 pistachios, shelled	Buffalo Chicken Bites (pg 136)	Slim-Fast Snack Bar	¼ cup banana chips
Spicy Red Lentil Vegetable Stew (pg 113)	Fajita Chicken Salad (pg 109)	Magically Moist Salmon with Light Mayonnaise (pg 17), Cuban Rice & Beans (pg 54), Grilled Red Tomatoes (pg 89)	Hearty Beef Barley Stew (pg 116)
Slim-Fast Snack Bar	Slim-Fast Snack Bar	Promise® Snack Mix (pg 124)	Cinnamon Caramel Corn (pg 132)

Slim·Fast!®
③·②·① Plan

Just follow the plan to lose weight, fast. Don't like one of the suggested snacks or balanced meals? Swap it for one you do. Just be sure the approximate calorie values are the same.

Week Three

	Day Fifteen	Day Sixteen	Day Seventeen
2 SHAKES OR MEAL BARS — **BREAKFAST**	Slim-Fast Shake or Meal Bar	Slim-Fast Shake or Meal Bar	Slim-Fast Shake or Meal Bar
3 SNACKS — **SNACK**	2 tangerines	Handful almonds (12 to 15 medium almonds)	1 cup blackberries
2 SHAKES OR MEAL BARS — **LUNCH**	Slim-Fast Shake or Meal Bar	Slim-Fast Shake or Meal Bar	Slim-Fast Shake or Meal Bar
3 SNACKS — **SNACK**	Slim-Fast Snack Bar	5 dried plums	Mediterranean Vegetable Bruschetta (pg 133)
1 BALANCED MEAL — **DINNER**	Tuscan Glazed Chicken (pg 30), Balsamic Berry Quinoa Salad (pg 43), Garlic Seasoned Green Beans (pg 88)	Balsamic Pork Medallions (pg 28), Holiday Butternut Squash with Apple & Cranberries (pg 61), Warm Portobello Mushroom Salad (pg 74)	Peanut Chicken Curry (pg 98)
3 SNACKS — **SNACK**	¾ cup sorbet	Slim-Fast Snack Bar	Slim-Fast Snack Bar

3 snacks, 2 Slim-Fast shakes or meal bars, 1 balanced meal

Day Eighteen	Day Nineteen	Day Twenty	Day Twenty-one
Slim-Fast Shake or Meal Bar	Slim-Fast Shake or Meal Bar	Slim-Fast Shake or Meal Bar	Slim-Fast Shake or Meal Bar
Slim-Fast Snack Bar	1 medium papaya	1 small mango	1½ cups fresh raspberries
Slim-Fast Shake or Meal Bar	Slim-Fast Shake or Meal Bar	Slim-Fast Shake or Meal Bar	Slim-Fast Shake or Meal Bar
2 cups cantaloupe pieces/balls	Huevos Rellenos (pg 141)	Slim-Fast Snack Bar	Bite-You-Back Roasted Edamame (pg 123)
Vegetarian Tacos (pg 112)	Veal Rolls with Basil (pg 41), Italian Quinoa Salad (pg 56), Roasted Cauliflower & Broccoli (pg 87)	Tilapia Gremolata (pg 115)	Parmesan Crusted Chicken (pg 25), Spicy Oven-Baked Fries (pg 57), Oven-Roasted Asparagus with Parmesan Gremolata (pg 72)
Black Pearl Hot 'N Spicy Chocolate Tea (pg 140)	Slim-Fast Snack Bar	Peppy Snack Mix (pg 127)	Slim-Fast Snack Bar

Slim·Fast! ®
③·②·① Plan

Just follow the plan to lose weight, fast. Don't like one of the suggested snacks or balanced meals? Swap it for one you do. Just be sure the approximate calorie values are the same.

Week Four

	Day Twenty-two	**Day Twenty-three**	**Day Twenty-four**
2 SHAKES OR MEAL BARS **BREAKFAST**	Slim-Fast Shake or Meal Bar	Slim-Fast Shake or Meal Bar	Slim-Fast Shake or Meal Bar
3 SNACKS **SNACK**	2 kiwis	¼ cup dried cranberries	Fruity Green Tea Smoothie (pg 135)
2 SHAKES OR MEAL BARS **LUNCH**	Slim-Fast Shake or Meal Bar	Slim-Fast Shake or Meal Bar	Slim-Fast Shake or Meal Bar
3 SNACKS **SNACK**	Slim-Fast Snack Bar	Wild Wedges (pg 125)	4 medium dates
1 BALANCED MEAL **DINNER**	Hidden Veggie Meatballs (pg 110)	Eggplant "Lasagna" (pg 94)	Savory Chicken Burgers (pg 107)
3 SNACKS **SNACK**	3½ cups light popcorn	Slim-Fast Snack Bar	Slim-Fast Snack Bar

3 snacks, 2 Slim-Fast shakes or meal bars, 1 balanced meal

Day Twenty-five	Day Twenty-six	Day Twenty-seven	Day Twenty-eight
Slim-Fast Shake or Meal Bar	Slim-Fast Shake or Meal Bar	Slim-Fast Shake or Meal Bar	Slim-Fast Shake or Meal Bar
2 Tbsp. raisins	1 cup cherries	1 whole-grain frozen waffle	2 clementines
Slim-Fast Shake or Meal Bar	Slim-Fast Shake or Meal Bar	Slim-Fast Shake or Meal Bar	Slim-Fast Shake or Meal Bar
Creamy Artichoke Bruschetta (pg 134)	½ cup strawberries with ½ cup plain yogurt	Slim-Fast Snack Bar	Slim-Fast Snack Bar
Asian Salmon Salad (pg 92)	Jamaican Pork with Creamy Lime Salsa (pg 18), Cilantro Rice with Tomatoes (pg 58), Berried Slaw (pg 77)	Vegged-Out Chili Bowls (pg 96)	Summer Panzanella Salad (pg 108)
Slim-Fast Snack Bar	Slim-Fast Snack Bar	¾ cup canned fruit in natural juice or light syrup	½ cup regular gelatin topped with 2 Tbsp. light Cool Whip®

Protein

magically moist salmon with light mayonnaise

MAKES:
4 servings

PREP TIME:
5 minutes

COOK TIME:
10 minutes

Nutrition Information per serving

Calories: 210

Calories From Fat: 110

Total Fat: 12g

Saturated Fat: 2g

Trans Fat: 0g

Cholesterol: 65mg

Sodium: 310mg

Total Carbohydrates: 1g

Dietary Fiber: 0g

Sugars: 0g

Protein: 23g

Vitamin A: 0%

Vitamin C: 0%

Calcium: 2%

Iron: 6%

4   salmon fillets (about 4 oz. ea.)

¼   cup Hellmann's® or Best Foods® Light Mayonnaise

¼   tsp. salt

⅛   tsp. ground black pepper

- Preheat oven to 400°F.
- Brush salmon with Hellmann's® or Best Foods® Light Mayonnaise, then season with salt and pepper. On baking pan, arrange salmon.
- Bake 10 minutes or until fish flakes with fork.

Also terrific with Hellmann's® or Best Foods® Canola Cholesterol Free Mayonnaise.

jamaican pork with creamy lime salsa

MAKES:
4 servings

PREP TIME:
10 minutes

COOK TIME:
15 minutes

Nutrition Information per serving

Calories: 250

Calories From Fat: 130

Total Fat: 15g

Saturated Fat: 3g

Trans Fat: 0g

Cholesterol: 70mg

Sodium: 510mg

Total Carbohydrates: 4g

Dietary Fiber: 0g

Sugars: 1g

Protein: 25g

Vitamin A: 0%

Vitamin C: 4%

Calcium: 4%

Iron: 4%

½ cup Hellmann's® or Best Foods® Light Mayonnaise

1 Tbsp. lime juice

¼ cup finely chopped red onion

1 clove garlic, finely chopped

¼ tsp. grated lime peel (optional)

⅛ tsp. ground black pepper

4 large boneless pork chops, ¾ inch thick* (1 lb.)

1 Tbsp. Jamaican jerk seasoning

1 medium mango, seeded, peeled and cut into 8 slices (optional)

Try substituting boneless chicken breasts or halibut steaks for pork chops.

• For Creamy Lime Salsa, combine Hellmann's® or Best Foods® Light Mayonnaise, lime juice, onion, garlic, lime peel, if desired, and pepper in medium bowl; set aside.

• Evenly season chops with jerk seasoning. Grill or broil chops until done. Arrange chops on serving platter, then evenly garnish with mango and Creamy Lime Salsa. Serve with remaining salsa.

Also terrific with Hellmann's® or Best Foods® Low Fat Mayonnaise Dressing or Hellmann's® or Best Foods® Canola Cholesterol Free Mayonnaise.

marinated chicken bruschetta

MAKES: 6 servings

PREP TIME: 10 minutes

MARINATE TIME: 30 minutes

COOK TIME: 12 minutes

Nutrition Information per serving

Calories: 170
Calories From Fat: 27
Total Fat: 3g
Saturated Fat: 0g
Trans Fat: 0g
Cholesterol: 65mg
Sodium: 390mg
Total Carbohydrates: 7g
Dietary Fiber: 1g
Sugars: 5g
Protein: 27g
Vitamin A: 10%
Vitamin C: 15%
Calcium: 2%
Iron: 6%

¾ cup Wish-Bone® Light Italian Dressing, divided

6 boneless, skinless chicken breasts (about 1½ lbs.)

2 medium beefsteak tomatoes, chopped

¼ cup diced red onion

1 Tbsp. finely chopped fresh basil leaves* (optional)

For Marinated Chicken with Fresh Salsa, use cilantro instead of basil.

• Pour ¼ cup Wish-Bone® Light Italian Dressing over chicken in large, shallow non-aluminum baking dish or plastic bag. Cover or close bag and marinate in refrigerator, turning occasionally, 30 minutes to 3 hours.

• Meanwhile, combine tomatoes, onion, basil and ¼ cup Wish-Bone® Light Italian Dressing in medium bowl. Cover and marinate in refrigerator at least 30 minutes.

• Remove chicken from marinade, discarding marinade. Grill or broil chicken, turning once and brushing frequently with remaining ¼ cup dressing, 12 minutes or until chicken is thoroughly cooked. Serve tomato bruschetta over chicken.

souperior meat loaf with bell peppers

MAKES:
8 servings

PREP TIME:
15 minutes

COOK TIME:
1 hour

Nutrition Information per serving

Calories: 240
Calories From Fat: 70
Total Fat: 8g
Saturated Fat: 3g
Trans Fat: 0g
Cholesterol: 125mg
Sodium: 600mg
Total Carbohydrates: 13g
Dietary Fiber: 1g
Sugars: 4g
Protein: 28g
Vitamin A: 4%
Vitamin C: 20%
Calcium: 4%
Iron: 20%

1   envelope Lipton® Recipe Secrets® Onion Soup Mix

2   lbs. lean ground beef

¾   cup plain dry bread crumbs*

2   eggs

¾   cup water

⅔   cup chopped green and/or red bell pepper

⅓   cup ketchup

You may also use 1½ cups fresh bread crumbs or 5 slices fresh bread, cubed.

- Preheat oven to 350°F. Combine all ingredients in large bowl.
- Shape into loaf in 13×9-inch baking or roasting pan.
- Bake uncovered 1 hour or until done. Let stand 10 minutes before serving.

SLOW COOKER METHOD: Arrange meat loaf in slow cooker. Cook covered on LOW 6 to 8 hours or HIGH 4 hours. (To help hold meat loaf together while lifting in and out of slow cooker, place meat loaf on a piece of cheesecloth, then on a rack.)

Also terrific with Lipton® Recipe Secrets® Beefy Onion Soup Mix, Lipton® Recipe Secrets® Onion Mushroom Soup Mix, Lipton® Recipe Secrets® Savory Herb with Garlic Soup Mix.

shrimp marinara

MAKES:
6 servings

PREP TIME:
10 minutes

COOK TIME:
10 minutes

Nutrition Information per serving

Calories: 230
Calories From Fat: 80
Total Fat: 9g
Saturated Fat: 1.5g
Trans Fat: 0g
Cholesterol: 170mg
Sodium: 740mg
Total Carbohydrates: 12g
Dietary Fiber: 2g
Sugars: 6g
Protein: 25g
Vitamin A: 15%
Vitamin C: 8%
Calcium: 8%
Iron: 20%

2   Tbsp. olive oil

⅛   to ¼ tsp. red pepper flakes

1½ lbs. large uncooked shrimp, peeled and deveined

2   cloves garlic, finely chopped OR ¼ tsp. garlic powder

1   jar (1 lb. 10 oz.) Ragu® Old World Style® Traditional Pasta Sauce
    Crusty Italian bread or hot cooked pasta (optional)

• Heat olive oil in 12-inch skillet over medium-high heat and cook red pepper flakes, stirring occasionally, 1 minute. Add shrimp and garlic and cook 3 minutes.

• Stir in Ragu® Old World Style® Traditional Pasta Sauce. Simmer 5 minutes or until shrimp are done and sauce is heated through.

• Serve, if desired, with crusty Italian bread or hot cooked pasta.

Buy ready-peeled shrimp and this recipe is ready in minutes!

new england cod

MAKES:
4 servings

PREP TIME:
5 minutes

COOK TIME:
12 minutes

Nutrition Information per serving

Calories: 220
Calories From Fat: 80
Total Fat: 9g
Saturated Fat: 2.5g
Trans Fat: 0g
Cholesterol: 50mg
Sodium: 290mg
Total Carbohydrates: 11g
Dietary Fiber: 0g
Sugars: 1g
Protein: 21g
Vitamin A: 15%
Vitamin C: 10%
Calcium: 4%
Iron: 6%

1   lb. cod, cut into 4 pieces

2   Tbsp. lemon juice

1   cup buttery cracker crumbs (about 20 crackers)

¼   cup I Can't Believe It's Not Butter!® Light Spread

1   Tbsp. chopped parsley, plus additional for garnish (optional)

    Lemon slices (optional)

• Preheat oven to 425°F. Spray 9-inch square baking dish with nonstick cooking spray. Arrange cod in prepared dish, then drizzle with lemon juice.

• Combine cracker crumbs, I Can't Believe It's Not Butter!® Light Spread and 1 tablespoon parsley in small bowl, then evenly sprinkle over cod.

• Bake 12 minutes or until cod flakes with a fork. Garnish, if desired, with additional chopped parsley and lemon slices.

TIP: Substitute another white fish for the cod, such as flounder, halibut, haddock or sole.

23
PROTEIN

honey mustard chicken fingers

MAKES:
5 servings

PREP TIME:
15 minutes

COOK TIME:
12 minutes

Nutrition Information per serving

Calories: 270

Calories From Fat: 70

Total Fat: 7g

Saturated Fat: 1g

Trans Fat: 0g

Cholesterol: 55mg

Sodium: 380mg

Total Carbohydrates: 26g

Dietary Fiber: 2g

Sugars: 7g

Protein: 25g

Vitamin A: 0%

Vitamin C: 2%

Calcium: 2%

Iron: 8%

6	Tbsp. Hellmann's® or Best Foods® Light Mayonnaise
1	Tbsp. Hellmann's® or Best Foods® Dijonnaise™ Creamy Dijon Mustard
2	Tbsp. honey
1	lb. boneless, skinless chicken breasts, cut into strips
1½	cups finely crushed corn flakes or whole wheat bread crumbs

• Preheat oven to 425°F. Combine Hellmann's® or Best Foods® Light Mayonnaise, Creamy Dijon Mustard and honey in medium bowl; reserve half for dipping.

• Add chicken to remaining mayonnaise mixture; stir to coat, then roll in crumbs.

• Bake 10 minutes or until chicken is thoroughly cooked. Serve with reserved honey mustard sauce.

parmesan crusted chicken

MAKES:
4 servings

PREP TIME:
10 minutes

COOK TIME:
20 minutes

Nutrition Information per serving

Calories: 280
Calories From Fat: 120
Total Fat: 13g
Saturated Fat: 2.5g
Trans Fat: 0g
Cholesterol: 95mg
Sodium: 460mg
Total Carbohydrates: 4g
Dietary Fiber: 0g
Sugars: 1g
Protein: 35g
Vitamin A: 2%
Vitamin C: 2%
Calcium: 8%
Iron: 6%

½ cup Hellmann's® or Best Foods® Light Mayonnaise

¼ cup grated Parmesan cheese

4 boneless, skinless chicken breasts (about 1¼ lbs.)

4 tsp. Italian seasoned dry bread crumbs

- Preheat oven to 425°F.

- Combine Hellmann's® or Best Foods® Light Mayonnaise with cheese in medium bowl. Arrange chicken on baking sheet. Evenly top with mayonnaise mixture, then sprinkle with bread crumbs.

- Bake 20 minutes or until chicken is thoroughly cooked.

1-2-3 chicken cacciatore

MAKES:
6 servings

PREP TIME:
5 minutes

COOK TIME:
30 minutes

Nutrition Information per serving

Calories: 290

Calories From Fat: 65

Total Fat: 7g

Saturated Fat: 1g

Trans Fat: 0g

Cholesterol: 90mg

Sodium: 610mg

Total Carbohydrates: 17g

Dietary Fiber: 2g

Sugars: 2g

Protein: 38g

Vitamin A: 0%

Vitamin C: 4%

Calcium: 8%

Iron: 6%

1	Tbsp. olive oil
2	lbs. boneless, skinless chicken breasts
1	jar (1 lb. 10 oz.) Ragú® Chunky Pasta Sauce
3	cups hot cooked rice

• Heat olive oil in 12-inch skillet over medium-high heat and brown chicken.

• Stir in Ragú® Chunky Pasta Sauce. Bring to a boil over high heat. Reduce heat to low and simmer covered 20 minutes or until chicken is thoroughly cooked.

• Serve with hot rice.

onion-apple glazed pork tenderloin

MAKES:
6 servings

PREP TIME:
5 minutes

COOK TIME:
25 minutes

Nutrition Information per serving

Calories: 230
Calories From Fat: 80
Total Fat: 9g
Saturated Fat: 2g
Trans Fat: 0.1g
Cholesterol: 75mg
Sodium: 480mg
Total Carbohydrates: 11g
Dietary Fiber: 0g
Sugars: 7g
Protein: 24g
Vitamin A: 0%
Vitamin C: 2%
Calcium: 2%
Iron: 8%

1½	to 2 lbs. pork tenderloin
	Ground black pepper
2	Tbsp. olive oil, divided
1	envelope Lipton® Recipe Secrets® Onion Soup Mix
½	cup apple juice
2	Tbsp. firmly packed brown sugar
¾	cup water
¼	cup dry red wine or water
1	Tbsp. all-purpose flour

• Preheat oven to 425°F. In small roasting or baking pan, arrange pork. Season with pepper and rub with 1 tablespoon olive oil. Roast uncovered 10 minutes.

• Meanwhile, in small bowl, combine remaining olive oil, Lipton® Recipe Secrets® Onion Soup Mix, apple juice and brown sugar. Pour over pork and continue roasting 10 minutes or until pork is done. Remove pork to serving platter; cover with aluminum foil.

• Place roasting pan over medium-high heat and bring pan juices to a boil, scraping up any brown bits from bottom of pan. Stir in water, wine and flour and boil, stirring constantly, 1 minute or until thickened. To serve, thinly slice pork and serve with gravy.

balsamic pork medallions

MAKES:
4 servings

PREP TIME:
15 minutes

COOK TIME:
7 minutes

Nutrition Information per serving

Calories: 280

Calories From Fat: 130

Total Fat: 15g

Saturated Fat: 3.5g

Trans Fat: 0g

Cholesterol: 75mg

Sodium: 350mg

Total Carbohydrates: 11g

Dietary Fiber: 0g

Sugars: 11g

Protein: 23g

Vitamin A: 0%

Vitamin C: 10%

Calcium: 2%

Iron: 10%

1   lb. pork tenderloin, cut into 8 slices and pounded lightly

½   tsp. finely chopped fresh rosemary leaves OR ¼ tsp. dried rosemary leaves, crushed

    Salt and ground black pepper (optional)

½   cup Wish-Bone® Light Balsamic Basil Vinaigrette Dressing

¼   cup orange juice

2   Tbsp. firmly packed brown sugar

1   Tbsp. olive oil

- Season pork with rosemary and, if desired, salt and pepper; set aside.

- Combine Wish-Bone® Light Balsamic Basil Vinaigrette Dressing, orange juice and brown sugar in small bowl; set aside.

- Heat olive oil in 12-inch nonstick skillet over medium-high heat and brown pork, turning once, 2 minutes. Stir in juice mixture and cook, stirring occasionally, 5 minutes or until pork is done. Serve pork with sauce.

tuscan glazed chicken

MAKES:
6 servings

PREP TIME:
10 minutes

COOK TIME:
20 minutes

Nutrition Information per serving

Calories: 240

Calories From Fat: 70

Total Fat: 8g

Saturated Fat: 1.5g

Trans Fat: 0g

Cholesterol: 95mg

Sodium: 290mg

Total Carbohydrates: 3g

Dietary Fiber: 0g

Sugars: 1g

Protein: 35g

Vitamin A: 4%

Vitamin C: 4%

Calcium: 2%

Iron: 8%

⅓ cup Hellmann's® or Best Foods® Mayonnaise Dressing with Extra Virgin Olive Oil

3 Tbsp. finely chopped roasted red peppers

1 tsp. garlic powder

½ tsp. dried Italian seasoning

1 tsp. balsamic vinegar

6 boneless, skinless chicken breasts (about 2 lbs.)

• Preheat oven to 425°F.

• Combine all ingredients except chicken in medium bowl. Arrange chicken on baking sheet, then evenly top with mayonnaise mixture.

• Bake 20 minutes or until chicken is thoroughly cooked.

This budget-friendly chicken is easily baked... and so moist!

grilled salmon with citrus salsa

MAKES:
4 servings

PREP TIME:
20 minutes

COOK TIME:
10 minutes

Nutrition Information per serving

Calories: 260

Calories From Fat: 90

Total Fat: 10g

Saturated Fat: 1.5g

Trans Fat: 0g

Cholesterol: 80mg

Sodium: 95mg

Total Carbohydrates: 14g

Dietary Fiber: 3g

Sugars: 9g

Protein: 29g

Vitamin A: 20%

Vitamin C: 100%

Calcium: 8%

Iron: 8%

2	large navel oranges, peeled, sectioned and coarsely chopped
2	medium tomatoes, chopped
⅔	cup sliced green onions
¼	cup chopped fresh cilantro
¼	tsp. hot pepper sauce
4	salmon fillets (about 1¼ lbs.)
20	sprays I Can't Believe It's Not Butter!® Spray Original

• Combine oranges, tomatoes, green onions, cilantro and hot pepper sauce in large bowl; set aside.

• Spray salmon with I Can't Believe It's Not Butter!® Spray Original and sprinkle, if desired, with salt and ground black pepper to taste. Grill or broil salmon, turning once, 10 minutes or until salmon is opaque. Serve salsa with salmon.

NOTE: Recipe can be halved.

spanish-style garlic shrimp

MAKES:
4 servings

PREP TIME:
20 minutes

COOK TIME:
10 minutes

Nutrition Information per serving

Calories: 170

Calories From Fat: 65

Total Fat: 7g

Saturated Fat: 2g

Trans Fat: 0g

Cholesterol: 170mg

Sodium: 540mg

Total Carbohydrates: 2g

Dietary Fiber: 0g

Sugars: 0g

Protein: 23g

Vitamin A: 15%

Vitamin C: 10%

Calcium: 6%

Iron: 15%

4	Tbsp. I Can't Believe It's Not Butter!® Light Spread, divided
1	lb. uncooked medium shrimp, peeled and deveined
½	tsp. salt
2	cloves garlic, finely chopped
½	to 1 jalapeño pepper, seeded and finely chopped
¼	cup chopped fresh cilantro or parsley
1	Tbsp. fresh lime juice

• Melt 1 tablespoon I Can't Believe It's Not Butter!® Light Spread in 12-inch nonstick skillet over high heat and cook shrimp with salt, turning once, 2 minutes or until shrimp are almost pink. Remove shrimp and set aside.

• Melt remaining 3 tablespoons Spread in same skillet over medium-low heat and cook garlic and jalapeño pepper, stirring occasionally, 1 minute. Return shrimp to skillet. Stir in cilantro and lime juice and heat 30 seconds or until shrimp turn pink.

pan-seared beef with shallot vinaigrette

MAKES:
4 servings

PREP TIME:
10 minutes

COOK TIME:
15 minutes

Nutrition Information per serving

Calories: 230
Calories From Fat: 70
Total Fat: 7g
Saturated Fat: 2.5g
Trans Fat: 0g
Cholesterol: 50mg
Sodium: 170mg
Total Carbohydrates: 8g
Dietary Fiber: 0g
Sugars: 2g
Protein: 27g
Vitamin A: 60%
Vitamin C: 6%
Calcium: 4%
Iron: 15%

2   Tbsp. I Can't Believe It's Not Butter!® Light Spread, divided

1   lb. lean top sirloin steak, trimmed

2   large shallots or 1 small onion, chopped (about 1 cup)

½   cup dry red wine

½   cup fat-free reduced-sodium beef broth

Freshly ground black pepper (optional)

• Melt 1 tablespoon I Can't Believe It's Not Butter!® Light Spread in 12-inch nonstick skillet over medium-high heat and cook steak, turning once, until desired doneness. Remove steak and thinly slice.

• Melt remaining Spread in same skillet and cook shallots, stirring occasionally, 4 minutes. Add wine and broth. Bring to a boil over high heat. Reduce heat to low and simmer, stirring occasionally, 5 minutes.

• Arrange sliced steak on serving platter, then drizzle with vinaigrette. Sprinkle, if desired, with ground black pepper.

33
PROTEIN

chicken piccata

4 servings

PREP TIME:
10 minutes

COOK TIME:
18 minutes

Nutrition Information per serving

Calories: 210

Calories From Fat: 45

Total Fat: 5g

Saturated Fat: 1.5g

Trans Fat: 0g

Cholesterol: 70mg

Sodium: 340mg

Total Carbohydrates: 9g

Dietary Fiber: 1g

Sugars: 0g

Protein: 28g

Vitamin A: 8%

Vitamin C: 8%

Calcium: 2%

Iron: 8%

⅓   cup all-purpose flour

¼   tsp. salt

¼   tsp. freshly ground black pepper

4   boneless, skinless chicken breasts (about 1 lb.), pounded

3   Tbsp. I Can't Believe It's Not Butter!® Light Spread, divided

½   cup fat-free, reduced-sodium chicken broth

4   thin slices lemon

    Parsley (optional)

• Combine flour, salt and pepper in shallow dish. Dip chicken in flour mixture, coating well.

• Melt 2 tablespoons I Can't Believe It's Not Butter!® Light Spread in 12-inch skillet over medium heat and cook chicken in 2 batches until chicken is thoroughly cooked, turning once. Remove chicken to serving platter and keep warm.

• Add broth and lemon slices to same skillet. Bring to a boil over high heat, scraping up brown bits from bottom of pan. Stir in remaining 1 tablespoon Spread until melted. Pour sauce over chicken and garnish, if desired, with parsley.

braised beef & mushrooms in cabernet sauce

MAKES:
8 servings

PREP TIME:
15 minutes

COOK TIME:
2 hours 30 minutes

Nutrition Information per serving

Calories: 270
Calories From Fat: 100
Total Fat: 11g
Saturated Fat: 3g
Trans Fat: 0g
Cholesterol: 65mg
Sodium: 390mg
Total Carbohydrates: 17g
Dietary Fiber: 2g
Sugars: 10g
Protein: 27g
Vitamin A: 70%
Vitamin C: 15%
Calcium: 4%
Iron: 20%

2 lbs. boneless chuck roast or stew meat, cut into 1-inch cubes
Salt and ground black pepper (optional)
¼ cup all-purpose flour
1 Tbsp. olive oil
2 medium onions, cut into wedges
1 pkg. (10 oz.) mushrooms, quartered
2 large carrots, sliced
1 clove garlic, finely chopped
1 jar Bertolli® Vineyard Premium Collections Fire Roasted Tomato with Cabernet Sauvignon Sauce
½ cup water

- Preheat oven to 375°F. Season beef, if desired, with salt and pepper, then toss with flour in large bowl.

- Heat olive oil in 12-inch nonstick skillet over medium-high heat and brown beef in 2 batches. Remove to 3-quart ovenproof casserole.

- Cook onions and mushrooms in same skillet, stirring occasionally, 5 minutes or until tender. Add carrots and garlic and cook 30 seconds. Stir in remaining ingredients, scraping up brown bits from bottom of pan. Turn into casserole; toss with beef. Bake covered 2 hours or until beef is tender.

buttery cilantro steak

MAKES:
4 servings

PREP TIME:
10 minutes

COOK TIME:
10 minutes

Nutrition Information per serving

Calories: 190

Calories From Fat: 50

Total Fat: 6g

Saturated Fat: 2g

Trans Fat: 0g

Cholesterol: 60mg

Sodium: 85mg

Total Carbohydrates: 0g

Dietary Fiber: 0g

Sugars: 0g

Protein: 31g

Vitamin A: 2%

Vitamin C: 0%

Calcium: 4%

Iron: 15%

1¼   lbs. boneless sirloin steak

10   sprays I Can't Believe It's Not Butter!® Spray Original

¼   cup chopped fresh cilantro

• Spray steak with I Can't Believe It's Not Butter!® Spray Original, then rub with cilantro. Grill or broil steaks, turning once, 10 minutes or until desired doneness. Let rest before slicing.

TIP: For a tasty variation, substitute pork tenderloin for the steak and use chopped fresh parsley, oregano or thyme instead of cilantro.

lemon flounder
with capers

MAKES:
4 servings

PREP TIME:
10 minutes

COOK TIME:
6 minutes

Nutrition Information per serving

Calories: 160

Calories From Fat: 40

Total Fat: 4g

Saturated Fat: 1g

Trans Fat: 0g

Cholesterol: 70mg

Sodium: 290mg

Total Carbohydrates: 2g

Dietary Fiber: 0g

Sugars: 0g

Protein: 27g

Vitamin A: 10%

Vitamin C: 15%

Calcium: 4%

Iron: 4%

2   Tbsp. I Can't Believe It's Not Butter!® Light Spread

2   cloves garlic, finely chopped

2   Tbsp. small capers, rinsed, drained and chopped

2   Tbsp. finely chopped fresh parsley

1   tsp. grated lemon peel

2   Tbsp. lemon juice

1¼ lbs. flounder or tilapia fillets

- Combine all ingredients except flounder in small bowl.

- Arrange flounder in jelly-roll or baking pan lined with aluminum foil, then sprayed with nonstick cooking spray. Top flounder with Spread mixture.

- Broil 6 minutes or until flounder flakes with fork. Serve with pan juices.

TIP: For Mexican Flounder, substitute chopped olives, chopped cilantro and lime juice for the capers, parsley and lemon juice.

chicken satay with spicy peanut sauce

MAKES: 4 servings

PREP TIME: 15 minutes

MARINATE TIME: 30 minutes

COOK TIME: 10 minutes

Nutrition Information per serving

Calories: 250

Calories From Fat: 80

Total Fat: 9g

Saturated Fat: 1.5g

Trans Fat: 0g

Cholesterol: 65mg

Sodium: 420mg

Total Carbohydrates: 6g

Dietary Fiber: 1g

Sugars: 7g

Protein: 30g

Vitamin A: 2%

Vitamin C: 2%

Calcium: 2%

Iron: 8%

½	cup Wish-Bone® Light Italian Dressing, divided
2	tsp. firmly packed brown sugar
3	tsp. finely chopped cilantro, divided
2	tsp. finely chopped fresh ginger
4	boneless, skinless chicken breasts (about 1 lb.), pounded thin and cut into thin strips
¼	cup Skippy® Reduced Fat Creamy Peanut Butter
¼	tsp. curry powder
¼	tsp. cayenne pepper

• For marinade, combine ¼ cup Wish-Bone® Light Italian Dressing, brown sugar, 2 teaspoons cilantro and ginger. In large, shallow non-aluminum baking dish or resealable plastic bag, pour 2 tablespoons marinade over chicken; turn to coat. Cover, or close bag, and marinate in refrigerator, turning occasionally, 30 minutes or up to 3 hours. Refrigerate remaining marinade.

• Meanwhile, in small bowl, blend Skippy® Reduced Fat Creamy Peanut Butter, remaining ¼ cup Dressing, 1 teaspoon cilantro, curry and cayenne pepper; refrigerate until ready to serve.

• Remove chicken from marinade, discarding marinade. On skewers, thread chicken. Grill or broil chicken, turning once and brushing frequently with refrigerated marinade, until chicken is thoroughly cooked. Serve with peanut sauce.

oven-fried rosemary chicken

MAKES:
8 servings

PREP TIME:
10 minutes

COOK TIME:
40 minutes

Nutrition Information per serving

Calories: 280
Calories From Fat: 90
Total Fat: 10g
Saturated Fat: 2g
Trans Fat: 0g
Cholesterol: 125mg
Sodium: 440mg
Total Carbohydrates: 6g
Dietary Fiber: 0g
Sugars: 1g
Protein: 37g
Vitamin A: 2%
Vitamin C: 6%
Calcium: 4%
Iron: 10%

½ cup plain dry bread crumbs
¾ tsp. seasoned salt
½ tsp. dried rosemary leaves, crushed
¼ tsp. ground black pepper
3½ lbs. chicken parts, skin removed
½ cup Hellmann's® or Best Foods® Light Mayonnaise

• Preheat oven to 400°F.

• Combine bread crumbs, seasoned salt, rosemary and pepper in shallow dish; set aside.

• Add chicken and Hellmann's® or Best Foods® Light Mayonnaise to large plastic bag; shake to evenly coat. Remove chicken, then lightly dip in crumb mixture. Arrange chicken on cookie sheet.

• Bake 40 minutes or until chicken is thoroughly cooked.

chicken margherita

MAKES:
4 servings

PREP TIME:
5 minutes

COOK TIME:
10 minutes

Nutrition Information per serving

Calories: 290

Calories From Fat: 110

Total Fat: 12g

Saturated Fat: 3g

Trans Fat: 0g

Cholesterol: 75mg

Sodium: 920mg

Total Carbohydrates: 13g

Dietary Fiber: 3g

Sugars: 6g

Protein: 32g

Vitamin A: 15%

Vitamin C: 2%

Calcium: 20%

Iron: 10%

4	boneless, skinless chicken breasts (about 1 lb.)
	Salt and freshly ground black pepper (optional)
1	Tbsp. olive oil
2	cups Ragu® Old World Style® Tomato Sauce
2	slices fresh or packaged mozzarella cheese (about 2 oz.)
2	Tbsp. thinly sliced fresh basil leaves

• Season chicken, if desired, with salt and pepper. Heat olive oil in 12-inch nonstick skillet over medium-high heat and brown chicken, turning once, about 5 minutes.

• Stir in Ragu® Old World Style® Tomato Sauce and simmer, covered, 5 minutes or until chicken is thoroughly cooked. Top chicken with cheese, then let stand until cheese is melted, about 1 minute. Garnish with basil.

For a little garlic flavor, season the chicken with a sprinkle of garlic powder in addition to the salt and pepper!

veal rolls
with basil

MAKES:
4 servings

PREP TIME:
15 minutes

COOK TIME:
50 minutes

**Nutrition
Information
per serving**

Calories: 250

Calories From Fat: 80

Total Fat: 9g

Saturated Fat: 2g

Trans Fat: 0g

Cholesterol: 95mg

Sodium: 310mg

Total Carbohydrates: 17g

Dietary Fiber: 3g

Sugars: 7g

Protein: 25g

Vitamin A: 30%

Vitamin C: 50%

Calcium: 8%

Iron: 10%

1	lb. veal cutlets
¼	tsp. salt
1	Tbsp. all-purpose flour
1½	Tbsp. olive oil
2	large onions, cut into wedges
3	cloves garlic, finely chopped
½	cup reduced-sodium chicken broth
¼	tsp. freshly ground black pepper
1	cup fresh basil leaves, cut into very thin strips, divided
4	medium very ripe tomatoes, quartered
	Fresh basil leaves (optional)

• Season veal with salt; roll up and secure with wooden toothpicks. Cut each roll in half crosswise, then lightly dust in flour.

• Heat olive oil in 12-inch skillet over medium-high heat and brown veal, about 5 minutes. Remove veal from skillet; set aside.

• In same skillet, cook onions, stirring occasionally, 6 minutes or until onions are golden. Stir in garlic and cook 30 seconds. Add broth and pepper. Bring to a boil over high heat. Reduce heat to low and simmer 2 minutes or until liquid is reduced by half. Return veal to skillet. Add ½ cup basil and simmer covered 20 minutes. Stir in tomatoes and remaining ½ cup basil. Simmer, covered, 20 minutes or until veal is tender. To serve, arrange veal on serving platter; remove toothpicks. Garnish, if desired, with fresh basil leaves.

Starch

balsamic berry quinoa salad

Nutrition Information per serving

Calories: 170
Calories From Fat: 40
Total Fat: 4.5g
Saturated Fat: 0.5g
Trans Fat: 0g
Cholesterol: 150mg
Sodium: 150mg
Total Carbohydrates: 28g
Dietary Fiber: 4g
Sugars: 7g
Protein: 5g
Vitamin A: 2%
Vitamin C: 35%
Calcium: 4%
Iron: 10%

2	cups water
1	cup quinoa
6	Tbsp. Wish-Bone® Light Balsamic Basil Vinaigrette Dressing
1	large cucumber, seeded and chopped
1	cup strawberries, quartered, or raspberries
1	Granny Smith apple, peeled, cored and chopped
¼	cup finely chopped red onion, rinsed with cold water

- Bring water to a boil over high heat in 2-quart saucepan. Stir in quinoa, then return to a boil. Reduce heat to medium and cook covered 12 minutes or until water is absorbed. Remove from heat, fluff, then let stand covered 15 minutes.

- Combine hot quinoa with remaining ingredients in serving bowl. Chill, if desired.

sweet 'n nutty orzo

MAKES:
6 servings

PREP TIME:
10 minutes

COOK TIME:
15 minutes

Nutrition Information per serving

Calories: 160
Calories From Fat: 40
Total Fat: 4.5g
Saturated Fat: 1g
Trans Fat: 0g
Cholesterol: 0mg
Sodium: 280mg
Total Carbohydrates: 26g
Dietary Fiber: 2g
Sugars: 2g
Protein: 5g
Vitamin A: 4%
Vitamin C: 2%
Calcium: 2%
Iron: 6%

3	Tbsp. chopped walnuts
2	Tbsp. I Can't Believe It's Not Butter!® Light Spread
1	small onion, chopped
1	clove garlic, finely chopped
¼	tsp. dried thyme leaves, crushed (optional)
¼	tsp. salt
⅛	tsp. ground black pepper
1	can (14½ oz.) fat-free, reduced-sodium chicken broth
1	cup uncooked orzo pasta
3	Tbsp. raisins
	Chopped fresh parsley (optional)

• Heat 10-inch nonstick skillet over medium-high heat. Add walnuts and cook 1 minute or until lightly browned. Remove walnuts and set aside.

• Melt I Can't Believe It's Not Butter!® Light Spread in same skillet over medium-high heat and cook onion, garlic, thyme, salt and pepper, stirring occasionally, 1 minute or until onion is almost tender. Add broth. Bring to a boil over high heat. Stir in orzo. Cook covered over medium heat, stirring occasionally, 10 minutes or until liquid is absorbed. Stir in raisins and walnuts. Garnish, if desired, with chopped fresh parsley.

sautéed polenta with sauce

MAKES:
4 servings

PREP TIME:
5 minutes

COOK TIME:
10 minutes

Nutrition Information per serving

Calories: 120

Calories From Fat: 35

Total Fat: 4g

Saturated Fat: 0.5g

Trans Fat: 0g

Cholesterol: 0mg

Sodium: 440mg

Total Carbohydrates: 19g

Dietary Fiber: 1g

Sugars: 4g

Protein: 3g

Vitamin A: 4%

Vitamin C: 2%

Calcium: 2%

Iron: 2%

8   slices (½-inch-thick) fat-free prepared polenta

    Salt and ground black pepper (optional)

1   Tbsp. olive oil

½   cup Bertolli® Vineyard Premium Collections Marinara with Burgundy Wine Sauce

• Season polenta, if desired, with salt and pepper. Heat olive oil in 12-inch nonstick skillet over medium heat and cook polenta, covered, turning once, 5 minutes or until golden. Add Bertolli® Vineyard Premium Collections Marinara with Burgundy Wine Sauce and cook covered 2 minutes or until heated through.

baked
squash

MAKES:
4 servings

PREP TIME:
10 minutes

COOK TIME:
45 minutes

Nutrition Information per serving

Calories: 160

Calories From Fat: 20

Total Fat: 2g

Saturated Fat: 0.5g

Trans Fat: 0g

Cholesterol: 0mg

Sodium: 55mg

Total Carbohydrates: 36g

Dietary Fiber: 4g

Sugars: 17g

Protein: 2g

Vitamin A: 410%

Vitamin C: 70%

Calcium: 10%

Iron: 10%

2	Tbsp. Promise® Buttery Light Spread, melted
2	Tbsp. pure maple syrup or pancake syrup
2	Tbsp. firmly packed brown sugar
½	tsp. ground cinnamon
1	medium butternut squash, halved and seeded
	Salt (optional)

- Preheat oven to 400°F. Lightly grease baking sheet; set aside.
- Combine all ingredients except squash in small bowl. Arrange squash cut side up on baking sheet; brush with half of the Spread mixture.
- Bake 45 minutes or until squash is tender, brushing with remaining Spread mixture halfway through cooking. Season, if desired, with salt.

curried whole wheat couscous

MAKES:
4 servings

PREP TIME:
5 minutes

COOK TIME:
10 minutes

Nutrition Information per serving

Calories: 120

Calories From Fat: 40

Total Fat: 4.5g

Saturated Fat: 1g

Trans Fat: 0g

Cholesterol: 0mg

Sodium: 420mg

Total Carbohydrates: 20g

Dietary Fiber: 3g

Sugars: 3g

Protein: 3g

Vitamin A: 0%

Vitamin C: 0%

Calcium: 2%

Iron: 4%

1	Tbsp. olive oil
1	tsp. curry powder
1	cup water
2	Tbsp. currants, raisins or golden raisins
1	Knorr® Vegetarian Vegetable Bouillon Cube, crumbled
⅔	cup plain whole wheat couscous
	Chopped fresh parsley (optional)

• Heat olive oil in 2-quart saucepan over medium heat and cook curry powder 30 seconds, stirring. Add water, currants and Knorr® Vegetarian Vegetable Bouillon Cube; bring to a boil over high heat. Reduce heat to low and simmer covered 2 minutes. Stir in couscous, then remove from heat. Let stand covered 5 minutes.

• Fluff couscous with fork before serving. Garnish, if desired, with chopped fresh parsley.

vegetable 'n bean pilaf

MAKES:
8 (½-cup) servings

PREP TIME:
10 minutes

COOK TIME:
20 to 30 minutes

Nutrition Information per serving

Calories: 110
Calories From Fat: 10
Total Fat: 1g
Saturated Fat: 0g
Trans Fat: 0g
Cholesterol: 0mg
Sodium: 410mg
Total Carbohydrates: 23g
Dietary Fiber: 3g
Sugars: 3g
Protein: 4g
Vitamin A: 30%
Vitamin C: 2%
Calcium: 2%
Iron: 8%

1⅓	cups water
½	cup uncooked regular rice
1	carrot, finely chopped
1	can (16 oz.) black-eyed peas, rinsed and drained
1	can (7 oz.) whole kernel corn, drained
⅓	cup Wish-Bone® Light Honey Dijon Dressing
2	tsp. chopped fresh parsley

• Bring water to a boil in 2-quart saucepan. Stir in uncooked rice and carrot. Simmer covered 20 minutes or until liquid is absorbed. Thoroughly stir in black-eyed peas, corn and Wish-Bone® Light Honey Dijon Dressing; heat through. Stir in parsley; serve immediately.

cuban
rice & beans

MAKES:
8 servings

PREP TIME:
10 minutes

COOK TIME:
25 minutes

Nutrition Information per serving

Calories: 150

Calories From Fat: 15

Total Fat: 1.5g

Saturated Fat: 0g

Trans Fat: 0g

Cholesterol: 0mg

Sodium: 260mg

Total Carbohydrates: 29g

Dietary Fiber: 3g

Sugars: 1g

Protein: 5g

Vitamin A: 4%

Vitamin C: 8%

Calcium: 4%

Iron: 8%

2	Tbsp. I Can't Believe It's Not Butter!® Light Spread, divided
1	cup finely chopped onion, divided
1	cup uncooked regular or converted rice
2	cups water
¼	tsp. salt
¼	cup finely chopped green bell pepper
1	can (about 15 oz.) black beans, undrained
1	Tbsp. chopped garlic
1	tsp. dried oregano leaves, crushed
	Cilantro (optional)

• Melt 1 tablespoon I Can't Believe It's Not Butter!® Light Spread in 3-quart saucepan over medium heat and cook ½ cup onion, stirring occasionally, 3 minutes or until tender. Add rice and cook, stirring frequently, 2 minutes or until rice is golden. Add water and salt and bring to a boil over high heat. Reduce heat to low and simmer covered 20 minutes or until rice is tender.

• Meanwhile, melt remaining 1 tablespoon Spread in 2-quart saucepan over medium heat and cook remaining ½ cup onion with green pepper, stirring occasionally, 5 minutes or until vegetables are tender. Stir in remaining ingredients and bring to a boil over high heat. Reduce heat to low and simmer, stirring occasionally, 3 minutes.

• Arrange rice on serving platter in a ring. Arrange vegetables in center of rice ring. Garnish, if desired, with cilantro.

black bean & corn ranch salad

MAKES:
5 servings

PREP TIME:
10 minutes

Nutrition Information per serving

Calories: 140

Calories From Fat: 20

Total Fat: 2g

Saturated Fat: 0g

Trans Fat: 0g

Cholesterol: 0mg

Sodium: 580mg

Total Carbohydrates: 25g

Dietary Fiber: 6g

Sugars: 6g

Protein: 5g

Vitamin A: 4%

Vitamin C: 15%

Calcium: 4%

Iron: 8%

½   cup Wish-Bone® Light Ranch Dressing

1   can (about 15 oz.) reduced-sodium black beans, rinsed and drained

1   can (11 oz.) whole kernel corn or mexi-corn, drained

1   cup quartered grape or cherry tomatoes

½   cup chopped red onion

2   Tbsp. chopped fresh cilantro

    Hot pepper sauce (optional)

    Lime wedges (optional)

- Combine all ingredients in medium bowl. Serve chilled or at room temperature. Garnish, if desired, with lime wedges.

italian
quinoa salad

MAKES: 4 servings

COOK TIME: 12 minutes

PREP TIME: 15 minutes

STAND TIME: 15 minutes

Nutrition Information per serving

Calories: 150

Calories From Fat: 30

Total Fat: 3.5g

Saturated Fat: 0g

Trans Fat: 0g

Cholesterol: 0mg

Sodium: 300mg

Total Carbohydrates: 24g

Dietary Fiber: 3g

Sugars: 4g

Protein: 5g

Vitamin A: 15%

Vitamin C: 50%

Calcium: 4%

Iron: 10%

1⅓	cups water
⅔	cup uncooked quinoa
½	cup Wish-Bone® Light Country Italian Dressing
½	cup chopped mushrooms
½	cup chopped red bell pepper
½	cup chopped zucchini
¼	cup green onions, sliced
1	Tbsp. chopped flat-leaf parsley

- Bring water to a boil over high heat in 2-quart saucepan. Add quinoa and return to a boil. Reduce heat to medium and cook, covered, 12 minutes or until water is absorbed. Remove from heat, fluff and let stand covered 15 minutes.

- Combine all remaining ingredients in serving bowl. Chill, if desired.

spicy oven-baked fries

MAKES:
6 servings

PREP TIME:
10 minutes

COOK TIME:
40 minutes

Nutrition Information per serving

Calories: 110
Calories From Fat: 30
Total Fat: 3.5g
Saturated Fat: 0.5g
Trans Fat: 0g
Cholesterol: 0mg
Sodium: 110mg
Total Carbohydrates: 18g
Dietary Fiber: 2g
Sugars: 1g
Protein: 2g
Vitamin A: 6%
Vitamin C: 15%
Calcium: 2%
Iron: 4%

1½	lbs. red potatoes, cut into wedges
3	Tbsp. Shedd's Spread Country Crock® Spread, melted
¼	tsp. seasoned salt
⅛	tsp. ground black pepper
¼	tsp. cayenne pepper

- Preheat oven to 450°F. Lightly grease baking sheet; set aside.

- In large bowl, toss all ingredients until potatoes are evenly coated. On prepared baking sheet, arrange potatoes in single layer. Bake, turning once, 40 minutes or until potatoes are golden brown and crisp.

cilantro rice
with tomatoes

MAKES:
6 servings

PREP TIME:
5 minutes

COOK TIME:
25 minutes

**Nutrition
Information
per serving**

Calories: 140

Calories From Fat: 30

Total Fat: 3g

Saturated Fat: 0.5g

Trans Fat: 0g

Cholesterol: 0mg

Sodium: 280mg

Total Carbohydrates: 26g

Dietary Fiber: 0g

Sugars: 1g

Protein: 3g

Vitamin A: 2%

Vitamin C: 6%

Calcium: 2%

Iron: 6%

1	Tbsp. vegetable oil
1	cup regular or converted rice
½	cup canned diced tomatoes
2	cups water
1	Tbsp. Knorr® reduced sodium Chicken flavor Bouillon
1	tsp. dried cilantro or parsley

• Heat oil in 12-inch nonstick skillet over medium-high heat and cook rice and tomatoes, stirring frequently, 3 minutes or until rice is golden. Stir in water, Knorr® reduced sodium Chicken flavor Bouillon and cilantro. Bring to a boil over high heat. Reduce heat to low and simmer, covered, 20 minutes or until rice is tender.

herb-crusted russet potatoes

MAKES:
6 servings

PREP TIME:
10 minutes

COOK TIME:
40 minutes

Nutrition Information per serving with Light Mayonnaise

Calories: 160
Calories From Fat: 40
Total Fat: 4.5g
Saturated Fat: 0.5g
Trans Fat: 0g
Cholesterol: 5mg
Sodium: 430mg
Total Carbohydrates: 29g
Dietary Fiber: 2g
Sugars: 1g
Protein: 3g
Vitamin A: 0%
Vitamin C: 15%
Calcium: 2%
Iron: 8%

⅓   cup Hellmann's® or Best Foods® Light Mayonnaise

1   Tbsp. finely chopped fresh rosemary OR 1 tsp. dried rosemary, crushed

2   tsp. finely chopped garlic

1   tsp. Kosher salt

¼   tsp. coarsely ground black pepper

2   lbs. russet potatoes, cut into 1-inch chunks

- Preheat oven to 425°F.

- In large bowl, combine all ingredients except potatoes. Add potatoes and toss to coat.

- In large shallow roasting pan, evenly spread potatoes. Roast, stirring once, 40 minutes or until potatoes are tender and golden brown.

savory skillet potatoes

MAKES:
4 servings

PREP TIME:
10 minutes

COOK TIME:
30 minutes

Nutrition Information per serving

Calories: 110
Calories From Fat: 25
Total Fat: 2.5g
Saturated Fat: 0.5g
Trans Fat: 0g
Cholesterol: 0mg
Sodium: 670mg
Total Carbohydrates: 18g
Dietary Fiber: 2g
Sugars: 1g
Protein: 2g
Vitamin A: 50%
Vitamin C: 20%
Calcium: 4%
Iron: 4%

2   Tbsp. I Can't Believe It's Not Butter!® Light Spread
¼   cup finely chopped onion or shallot
1   Tbsp. finely chopped sun-dried tomatoes
1   tsp. finely chopped fresh thyme leaves
¼   tsp. salt
    Pinch ground white pepper
2   cans (14½ oz. ea.) whole new potatoes, drained and thinly sliced

• In 12-inch nonstick skillet, melt I Can't Believe It's Not Butter!® Light Spread over medium-high heat and cook onion, stirring occasionally, 2 minutes or until onion is tender. Stir in sun-dried tomatoes, thyme, salt and pepper. Stir in potatoes, tossing to coat. Cook over medium heat, stirring occasionally, 25 minutes or until potatoes are golden brown. (Potatoes will begin to stick and break apart.)

holiday butternut squash with apple & cranberries

MAKES:
4 servings

PREP TIME:
15 minutes

COOK TIME:
45 minutes

Nutrition Information per serving

Calories: 160

Calories From Fat: 30

Total Fat: 3g

Saturated Fat: 1g

Trans Fat: 0g

Cholesterol: 0mg

Sodium: 55mg

Total Carbohydrates: 34g

Dietary Fiber: 4g

Sugars: 19g

Protein: 2g

Vitamin A: 300%

Vitamin C: 50%

Calcium: 8%

Iron: 6%

2	Tbsp. Shedd's Spread Country Crock® Light Spread, melted
4	cups cubed butternut squash
1	small apple, cubed
¼	cup dried cranberries
¼	tsp. ground cinnamon
¼	tsp. ground nutmeg (optional)
2	Tbsp. firmly packed brown sugar

- Preheat oven to 425°F.

- Combine all ingredients in 1½-quart baking dish. Season, if desired, with salt. Cover and bake 30 minutes. Remove cover and bake an additional 15 minutes or until squash is tender.

spicy sweet potato rounds

MAKES:
4 servings

PREP TIME:
10 minutes

COOK TIME:
30 minutes

Nutrition Information per serving

Calories: 130
Calories From Fat: 15
Total Fat: 1.5g
Saturated Fat: 0g
Trans Fat: 0g
Cholesterol: 0mg
Sodium: 360mg
Total Carbohydrates: 26g
Dietary Fiber: 3g
Sugars: 7g
Protein: 2g
Vitamin A: 320%
Vitamin C: 8%
Calcium: 4%
Iron: 4%

1   lb. sweet potatoes or yams, peeled and sliced into ¼-inch rounds

½   cup Wish-Bone® Light Country Italian Dressing

¼   tsp. cayenne pepper

• Preheat oven to 450°F. Combine all ingredients in medium bowl. Spread in single layer on jelly-roll pan. Bake, stirring twice, 30 minutes or until potatoes are crisp.

veggie brown rice & orzo pilaf

MAKES: 10 servings

PREP TIME: 15 minutes

COOK TIME: 35 minutes

Nutrition Information per serving

Calories: 150
Calories From Fat: 20
Total Fat: 2g
Saturated Fat: 0g
Trans Fat: 0g
Cholesterol: 0mg
Sodium: 55mg
Total Carbohydrates: 30g
Dietary Fiber: 2g
Sugars: 2g
Protein: 4g
Vitamin A: 35%
Vitamin C: 50%
Calcium: 2%
Iron: 6%

2	Tbsp. I Can't Believe It's Not Butter!® Light Spread
1	small onion, chopped
2	medium red, yellow and/or orange bell peppers, finely chopped
1	carrot, finely chopped
⅛	tsp. salt
⅛	tsp. ground black pepper
⅛	tsp. dried thyme leaves, crushed
1	cup uncooked brown rice
2¼	cups fat-free, reduced-sodium chicken broth
1	cup uncooked orzo pasta, prepared according to package directions
2	Tbsp. finely chopped fresh parsley (optional)

- Melt I Can't Believe It's Not Butter!® Light Spread in 3-quart saucepot over medium-high heat and cook onion, red peppers, carrot, salt, pepper and thyme, stirring frequently, 4 minutes or until vegetables are tender. Stir in rice and cook 3 minutes. Add broth and bring to a boil over high heat. Reduce heat to low and simmer, covered, 25 minutes or until rice is tender. Let stand 5 minutes. Stir in hot orzo and, if desired, parsley.

Vegetables

baked stuffed zucchini

MAKES:
4 servings

PREP TIME:
10 minutes

COOK TIME:
35 minutes

**Nutrition
Information
per serving**

Calories: 110

Calories From Fat: 10

Total Fat: 1g

Saturated Fat: 0g

Trans Fat: 0g

Cholesterol: 10mg

Sodium: 90mg

Total Carbohydrates: 21g

Dietary Fiber: 1g

Sugars: 1g

Protein: 4g

Vitamin A: 2%

Vitamin C: 4%

Calcium: 2%

Iron: 2%

2	medium zucchini, halved lengthwise
1	Tbsp. olive oil
1	clove garlic, finely chopped
½	cup chopped onion
½	cup chopped mushrooms
¼	cup Ragú® Old World Style® Traditional Pasta Sauce
2	Tbsp. panko or fresh bread crumbs

• Preheat oven to 375°F. Scoop out pulp from zucchini halves, then chop zucchini pulp and set aside. Arrange zucchini halves on baking sheet; set aside.

• Heat olive oil in 12-inch skillet over medium heat and cook garlic and onion, stirring occasionally, 1 minute. Add chopped zucchini and mushrooms and cook, stirring occasionally, 5 minutes or until tender. Stir in Ragú® Old World Style® Traditional Pasta Sauce; heat through. Evenly fill zucchini with vegetable mixture, then top with bread crumbs. Bake 30 minutes or until zucchini are tender.

mediterranean tomato salad

MAKES:
6 servings

PREP TIME:
10 minutes

CHILL TIME:
30 minutes

Nutrition Information per serving

Calories: 80

Calories From Fat: 35

Total Fat: 4g

Saturated Fat: 0.5g

Trans Fat: 0g

Cholesterol: 0mg

Sodium: 210mg

Total Carbohydrates: 12g

Dietary Fiber: 3g

Sugars: 8g

Protein: 2g

Vitamin A: 40%

Vitamin C: 50%

Calcium: 4%

Iron: 4%

3   lbs. assorted tomatoes (plum, yellow or beefsteak), cut into wedges OR cherry tomatoes, halved

1   large shallot or small onion, finely chopped

¼   cup loosely packed fresh basil leaves, cut into thin strips

½   cup Wish-Bone® Light Balsamic Vinaigrette Dressing

Shaved Parmesan cheese (optional)

- Toss all ingredients except cheese in large bowl. Cover and refrigerate at least 30 minutes.
- Just before serving, if desired, garnish with shaved Parmesan cheese.

grilled ratatouille

MAKES:
6 servings

PREP TIME:
15 minutes

COOK TIME:
15 minutes

Nutrition Information per serving

Calories: 80
Calories From Fat: 20
Total Fat: 2g
Saturated Fat: 1g
Trans Fat: 0g
Cholesterol: 0mg
Sodium: 45mg
Total Carbohydrates: 15g
Dietary Fiber: 6g
Sugars: 8g
Protein: 3g
Vitamin A: 50%
Vitamin C: 170%
Calcium: 4%
Iron: 6%

1½ Tbsp. I Can't Believe It's Not Butter!® Light Spread
1   tsp. fresh thyme leaves OR ¼ tsp. dried thyme leaves, crushed
1   tsp. grated lemon peel
1   tsp. lemon juice
2   large zucchini and/or yellow squash, halved lengthwise
2   medium tomatoes, halved
1   small eggplant, cut into ½-inch-thick slices
2   large red bell peppers, cut into large chunks
1   medium red onion, cut into ½-inch-thick slices

• Microwave I Can't Believe It's Not Butter!® Light Spread, thyme, lemon peel and lemon juice in small microwave-safe bowl on HIGH 20 seconds or until Spread is melted.

• Grill vegetables, turning occasionally and brushing with Spread mixture, 10 minutes or until vegetables are tender; coarsely chop.

veggie "spaghetti" & sauce

MAKES:
4 servings

PREP TIME:
5 minutes

COOK TIME:
4 minutes

Nutrition Information per serving

Calories: 110

Calories From Fat: 30

Total Fat: 3.5g

Saturated Fat: 1g

Trans Fat: 0g

Cholesterol: 5mg

Sodium: 670mg

Total Carbohydrates: 15g

Dietary Fiber: 5g

Sugars: 9g

Protein: 5g

Vitamin A: 70%

Vitamin C: 110%

Calcium: 10%

Iron: 8%

1   bag (12 oz.) broccoli slaw

1   Tbsp. water

2   cups Ragu® Organic Garden Veggie Pasta Sauce*, heated

2   Tbsp. grated Parmesan cheese

Also terrific with Ragu® Old World Style® Pasta Sauce.

• Microwave broccoli slaw with water in microwave-safe bowl, covered, on HIGH 4 minutes or until crisp-tender, stirring once halfway through. Carefully remove cover; drain.

• Top with Ragu® Organic Garden Veggie Pasta Sauce, then sprinkle with cheese.

TIP: Chop up additional veggies and sneak them into the sauce for even more veggies in this meal.

oven-roasted asparagus with parmesan gremolata

MAKES:
2 servings

PREP TIME:
10 minutes

COOK TIME:
15 minutes

Nutrition Information per serving

Calories: 110
Calories From Fat: 35
Total Fat: 3.5g
Saturated Fat: 1g
Trans Fat: 0g
Cholesterol: 0mg
Sodium: 60mg
Total Carbohydrates: 17g
Dietary Fiber: 5g
Sugars: 6g
Protein: 7g
Vitamin A: 40%
Vitamin C: 30%
Calcium: 8%
Iron: 30%

2	tsp. finely chopped fresh parsley
2	tsp. grated Parmesan cheese
¼	tsp. grated lemon peel
1	lb. asparagus, trimmed
2	large shallots, cut into thin wedges or ⅓ cup thinly sliced onion
1	Tbsp. Promise® Buttery Light Spread, melted
	Freshly ground black pepper (optional)

- Preheat oven to 425°F.

- Combine parsley, cheese and lemon peel in small bowl; set aside.

- Toss asparagus, shallots and Promise® Buttery Light Spread in 13×9-inch roasting pan. Roast 15 minutes or until tender.

- Arrange asparagus mixture on serving platter, then top with cheese mixture. Season, if desired, with pepper.

buttery citrus sautéed vegetables

MAKES:
4 servings

PREP TIME:
15 minutes

COOK TIME:
10 minutes

Nutrition Information per serving

Calories: 70
Calories From Fat: 40
Total Fat: 4.5g
Saturated Fat: 0.5g
Trans Fat: 0g
Cholesterol: 0mg
Sodium: 65mg
Total Carbohydrates: 8g
Dietary Fiber: 3g
Sugars: 4g
Protein: 3g
Vitamin A: 15%
Vitamin C: 70%
Calcium: 4%
Iron: 4%

3   Tbsp. Promise® Buttery Light Spread

2   lbs. your favorite vegetables (red onions, zucchini, asparagus, bell peppers), coarsely chopped

¼   cup loosely packed flat-leaf parsley, chopped (optional)

1   clove garlic, finely chopped

½   tsp. grated lemon peel

• Heat Promise® Buttery Light Spread in 12-inch nonstick skillet; cook vegetables until crisp-tender. Combine parsley, if desired, garlic and lemon peel in small bowl; evenly sprinkle over vegetables in skillet; cook 1 minute longer.

warm portobello mushroom salad

MAKES:
4 servings

PREP TIME:
10 minutes

COOK TIME:
10 minutes

Nutrition Information per serving

Calories: 70

Calories From Fat: 40

Total Fat: 4.5g

Saturated Fat: 0.5g

Trans Fat: 0g

Cholesterol: 0mg

Sodium: 20mg

Total Carbohydrates: 6g

Dietary Fiber: 2g

Sugars: 3g

Protein: 2g

Vitamin A: 30%

Vitamin C: 2%

Calcium: 0%

Iron: 4%

1	Tbsp. olive oil
8	oz. portobello mushrooms, thinly sliced
1	green onion, sliced
6	cups mesclun or mixed salad greens (about 6 oz.)
1/8	tsp. cracked black pepper
40	sprays Wish-Bone® Salad Spritzers® Balsamic Breeze® Vinaigrette Dressing

• Heat olive oil in 12-inch nonstick skillet over medium-high heat and cook mushrooms, stirring occasionally, 10 minutes or until mushrooms are tender. Stir in green onion and keep warm.

• On serving plates, arrange greens, then top with mushrooms and sprinkle with pepper. Just before serving, spritz with Wish-Bone® Salad Spritzers® Balsamic Breeze® Vinaigrette Dressing.

vegetable medley sauté

MAKES:
4 servings

PREP TIME:
10 minutes

COOK TIME:
6 minutes

Nutrition Information per serving

Calories: 100

Calories From Fat: 25

Total Fat: 3g

Saturated Fat: 1g

Trans Fat: 0g

Cholesterol: 0mg

Sodium: 250mg

Total Carbohydrates: 16g

Dietary Fiber: 6g

Sugars: 8g

Protein: 3g

Vitamin A: 320%

Vitamin C: 350%

Calcium: 6%

Iron: 6%

2   Tbsp. I Can't Believe It's Not Butter!® Light Spread

2   cups sliced carrots

3   large red bell peppers, sliced

3   cups broccoli florets

1   clove garlic, finely chopped

2   tsp. chopped fresh parsley (optional)

¼   tsp. salt

⅛   tsp. ground black pepper

• Melt I Can't Believe It's Not Butter!® Light Spread in 12-inch nonstick skillet over medium-high heat and cook carrots, red bell pepper and broccoli, stirring occasionally, 6 minutes or until crisp-tender. Stir in garlic and cook 30 seconds. Stir in parsley, if desired, and heat through. Season with salt and ground black pepper.

berried slaw

Nutrition Information per serving

Calories: 140
Calories From Fat: 45
Total Fat: 5g
Saturated Fat: 0.5g
Trans Fat: 0g
Cholesterol: 0mg
Sodium: 220mg
Total Carbohydrates: 20g
Dietary Fiber: 4g
Sugars: 10g
Protein: 4g
Vitamin A: 15%
Vitamin C: 110%
Calcium: 10%
Iron: 6%

1   bag (24 oz.) coleslaw mix
1   can (11 oz.) mandarin oranges, drained
¼   cup red onion, thinly sliced
½   cup Wish-Bone® Light Raspberry Walnut Vinaigrette Dressing
¼   cup nonfat plain yogurt
¼   cup toasted sliced almonds (optional)

- In large bowl, combine all ingredients except almonds. Serve chilled or at room temperature. Just before serving, if desired, stir in almonds.

italian steamed broccoli

MAKES:
4 servings

PREP TIME:
8 minutes

COOK TIME:
5 minutes

Nutrition Information per serving

Calories: 70
Calories From Fat: 15
Total Fat: 1.5g
Saturated Fat: 0g
Trans Fat: 0g
Cholesterol: 0mg
Sodium: 270mg
Total Carbohydrates: 12g
Dietary Fiber: 6g
Sugars: 2g
Protein: 6g
Vitamin A: 120%
Vitamin C: 290%
Calcium: 8%
Iron: 10%

10	cups broccoli florets
2	Tbsp. water
¼	cup Wish-Bone® Light Italian Dressing
3	Tbsp. roasted red peppers, chopped

- Microwave broccoli with water in microwave-safe 2-quart casserole with lid at HIGH 5 minutes or until tender; drain. Stir in Wish-Bone® Light Italian Dressing and peppers.

grilled green beans

MAKES:
4 servings

PREP TIME:
10 minutes

COOK TIME:
10 minutes

Nutrition Information per serving

Calories: 90

Calories From Fat: 25

Total Fat: 2.5g

Saturated Fat: 0.5g

Trans Fat: 0g

Cholesterol: 0mg

Sodium: 50mg

Total Carbohydrates: 15g

Dietary Fiber: 4g

Sugars: 6g

Protein: 3g

Vitamin A: 70%

Vitamin C: 35%

Calcium: 4%

Iron: 8%

1	lb. green beans, trimmed
2	shallots or 1 small onion, cut into wedges
1	Tbsp. apple cider vinegar
1	Tbsp. honey
2	Tbsp. I Can't Believe It's Not Butter!® Light Spread, divided

• Combine all ingredients except 1 tablespoon I Can't Believe It's Not Butter!® Light Spread in center of 30×18-inch sheet heavy-duty aluminum foil. Wrap foil loosely around mixture, sealing edges airtight with double fold. Place on another 30×18-inch sheet of foil; seal edges airtight with double fold in opposite direction. Grill, shaking package occasionally and turning package once, 10 minutes or until green beans are tender. Top with remaining 1 tablespoon Spread.

sautéed snow peas & baby carrots

MAKES:
2 servings

PREP TIME:
5 minutes

COOK TIME:
6 minutes

Nutrition Information per serving

Calories: 130

Calories From Fat: 20

Total Fat: 2.5g

Saturated Fat: 1g

Trans Fat: 0g

Cholesterol: 0mg

Sodium: 150mg

Total Carbohydrates: 20g

Dietary Fiber: 6g

Sugars: 12g

Protein: 4g

Vitamin A: 100%

Vitamin C: 4%

Calcium: 8%

Iron: 0%

1	Tbsp. I Can't Believe It's Not Butter!® Light Spread
2	Tbsp. chopped shallots or onion
10	oz. frozen whole baby carrots, partially thawed
3	cups snow peas
2	tsp. chopped fresh parsley (optional)

• Melt I Can't Believe It's Not Butter!® Light Spread in 12-inch nonstick skillet over medium heat and cook shallots, stirring occasionally, 1 minute or until almost tender. Add carrots and snow peas and cook, stirring occasionally, 4 minutes or until crisp-tender. If desired, stir in parsley and heat through.

savory balsamic asparagus

MAKES:
4 servings

PREP TIME:
5 minutes

COOK TIME:
15 minutes

Nutrition Information per serving

Calories: 700

Calories From Fat: 10

Total Fat: 1g

Saturated Fat: 0g

Trans Fat: 0g

Cholesterol: 0mg

Sodium: 180mg

Total Carbohydrates: 10g

Dietary Fiber: 5g

Sugars: 5g

Protein: 5g

Vitamin A: 35%

Vitamin C: 20%

Calcium: 6%

Iron: 25%

2	lbs. asparagus, trimmed
30	sprays I Can't Believe It's Not Butter!® Spray Original
2	Tbsp. balsamic vinegar (optional)
¼	tsp. salt
⅛	tsp. ground black pepper

- Preheat oven to 425°F.

- Arrange asparagus in roasting pan; evenly spray with I Can't Believe It's Not Butter!® Spray Original. Roast 15 minutes or until asparagus are crisp-tender. Drizzle with vinegar, if desired, and season with salt and pepper. Serve warm or at room temperature.

toasted corn & zucchini sauté

MAKES:
4 servings

PREP TIME:
15 minutes

COOK TIME:
10 minutes

Nutrition Information per serving

Calories: 90

Calories From Fat: 10

Total Fat: 1g

Saturated Fat: 0g

Trans Fat: 0g

Cholesterol: 0mg

Sodium: 80mg

Total Carbohydrates: 20g

Dietary Fiber: 3g

Sugars: 3g

Protein: 4g

Vitamin A: 30%

Vitamin C: 120%

Calcium: 2%

Iron: 4%

1	pkg. (10 oz.) frozen whole kernel corn, thawed
1	large zucchini, finely chopped
1	large orange bell pepper, finely chopped
1	clove garlic, finely chopped
20	sprays I Can't Believe It's Not Butter!® Spray Original
½	cup fat-free reduced-sodium chicken broth
1	Tbsp. chopped fresh cilantro (optional)
⅛	tsp. ground black pepper

• Spray corn, zucchini, orange bell pepper and garlic with I Can't Believe It's Not Butter!® Spray Original in large bowl; toss to coat.

• Cook vegetable mixture in preheated 10-inch nonstick skillet over medium-high heat, stirring occasionally, 5 minutes or until corn is golden. Add broth. Bring to a boil over high heat. Reduce heat to low and simmer, covered, 5 minutes or until corn is tender. Stir in cilantro, if desired, and ground black pepper.

rich & creamy
mashed cauliflower

MAKES:
5 servings

PREP TIME:
5 minutes

COOK TIME:
15 minutes

Nutrition Information per serving

Calories: 90

Calories From Fat: 40

Total Fat: 4g

Saturated Fat: 0.5g

Trans Fat: 0g

Cholesterol: 5mg

Sodium: 270mg

Total Carbohydrates: 12g

Dietary Fiber: 5g

Sugars: 5g

Protein: 4g

Vitamin A: 2%

Vitamin C: 160%

Calcium: 4%

Iron: 6%

1½ qts. water

2 medium heads cauliflower, separated into florets (about 10 cups)

2 cloves garlic, peeled (optional)

¼ cup Hellmann's® or Best Foods® Light Mayonnaise

¼ tsp. salt

1 Tbsp. chopped fresh basil leaves (optional)

• In 3-quart saucepot, bring water to a boil. Add cauliflower and garlic, if desired, and cook, covered, 15 minutes or until florets are tender; drain.

• In food processor or blender, process cauliflower, garlic, Hellmann's® or Best Foods® Light Mayonnaise and salt until creamy, scraping down sides as needed. Stir in basil, if desired, and serve immediately.

savory braised green beans & red pepper

MAKES:
4 servings

PREP TIME:
10 minutes

COOK TIME:
9 minutes

Nutrition Information per serving

Calories: 80

Calories From Fat: 30

Total Fat: 3.5g

Saturated Fat: 0g

Trans Fat: 0g

Cholesterol: 0mg

Sodium: 90mg

Total Carbohydrates: 12g

Dietary Fiber: 5g

Sugars: 3g

Protein: 4g

Vitamin A: 45%

Vitamin C: 120%

Calcium: 6%

Iron: 8%

1	lb. green beans
1	large red bell pepper, thinly sliced
2	cloves garlic, finely chopped
30	sprays I Can't Believe It's Not Butter!® Spray Original
½	cup fat-free reduced-sodium chicken or vegetable broth
3	Tbsp. sliced almonds, lightly toasted
	Ground black pepper (optional)

• Spray green beans, red bell pepper and garlic with I Can't Believe It's Not Butter!® Spray Original in large bowl; toss to coat.

• Cook vegetable mixture in preheated 12-inch nonstick skillet over medium-high heat, stirring occasionally, 3 minutes. Add broth. Bring to a boil over high heat. Reduce heat to medium and simmer, stirring occasionally, 6 minutes or until vegetables are crisp-tender. Sprinkle with almonds and season, if desired, with ground black pepper.

corn salsa

MAKES:
4 servings

PREP TIME:
15 minutes

MARINATE TIME:
30 minutes

Nutrition Information per serving

Calories: 100

Calories From Fat: 20

Total Fat: 2g

Saturated Fat: 0g

Trans Fat: 0g

Cholesterol: 0mg

Sodium: 450mg

Total Carbohydrates: 16g

Dietary Fiber: 3g

Sugars: 8g

Protein: 2g

Vitamin A: 8%

Vitamin C: 20%

Calcium: 2%

Iron: 4%

⅓ cup Wish-Bone® Light Italian Dressing

1 can (11 oz.) whole kernel corn, drained (about 1½ cups)

1 medium tomato, diced (about 1 cup)

1 medium cucumber, peeled, seeded and diced (about 1 cup)

¼ cup diced red onion

4 tsp. finely chopped jalapeño pepper or hot pepper sauce to taste (optional)

1 Tbsp. finely chopped fresh cilantro (optional)

1 tsp. grated lime peel

• Combine all ingredients in medium bowl. Cover and marinate in refrigerator at least 30 minutes. Serve chilled or at room temperature with your favorite grilled foods.

honey dijon spinach salad

Nutrition Information per serving

Calories: 110

Calories From Fat: 15

Total Fat: 1.5g

Saturated Fat: 0g

Trans Fat: 0g

Cholesterol: 0mg

Sodium: 280mg

Total Carbohydrates: 23g

Dietary Fiber: 5g

Sugars: 12g

Protein: 3g

Vitamin A: 80%

Vitamin C: 100%

Calcium: 6%

Iron: 15%

1	pkg. (10 oz.) fresh spinach leaves, rinsed and drained (about 7 cups)
1	can (11 oz.) mandarin oranges, drained
½	cup chopped onion
1	small red or green bell pepper, sliced
⅓	cup Wish-Bone® Light Honey Dijon Dressing

- In large bowl, combine all ingredients except Wish-Bone® Light Honey Dijon Dressing. Add Dressing and toss gently.

roasted cauliflower & broccoli

MAKES:
4 servings

PREP TIME:
10 minutes

COOK TIME:
25 minutes

Nutrition Information per serving

Calories: 90

Calories From Fat: 25

Total Fat: 3g

Saturated Fat: 0.5g

Trans Fat: 0g

Cholesterol: 0mg

Sodium: 170mg

Total Carbohydrates: 15g

Dietary Fiber: 5g

Sugars: 6g

Protein: 4g

Vitamin A: 45%

Vitamin C: 190%

Calcium: 6%

Iron: 6%

8 cups broccoli and/or cauliflower florets

6 cloves garlic

¼ cup Wish-Bone® Red Wine Vinaigrette Dressing

- Preheat oven to 400°F.

- Toss all ingredients in large bowl. Spread in single layer on jelly-roll pan. Roast, stirring once, 25 minutes or until golden.

garlic seasoned green beans

MAKES:
4 servings

PREP TIME:
10 minutes

COOK TIME:
5 minutes

Nutrition Information per serving

Calories: 60

Calories From Fat: 20

Total Fat: 2.5g

Saturated Fat: 0.5g

Trans Fat: 0g

Cholesterol: 0mg

Sodium: 260mg

Total Carbohydrates: 7g

Dietary Fiber: 3g

Sugars: 4g

Protein: 1g

Vitamin A: 6%

Vitamin C: 8%

Calcium: 6%

Iron: 2%

1   lb. green beans, trimmed

½   cup water

1   Tbsp. I Can't Believe It's Not Butter!® Light Spread

½   tsp. garlic salt

- Combine green beans and water in microwave-safe casserole. Microwave partially covered on HIGH 5 minutes or until beans are crisp-tender; drain.

- In medium bowl, gently toss beans, Spread and garlic salt.

grilled red tomatoes

MAKES:
8 servings

PREP TIME:
10 minutes

COOK TIME:
8 minutes

Nutrition Information per serving

Calories: 100
Calories From Fat: 40
Total Fat: 4g
Saturated Fat: 0.5g
Trans Fat: 0g
Cholesterol: 5mg
Sodium: 480mg
Total Carbohydrates: 14g
Dietary Fiber: 2g
Sugars: 4g
Protein: 3g
Vitamin A: 15%
Vitamin C: 20%
Calcium: 2%
Iron: 6%

⅓	cup Hellmann's® or Best Foods® Light Mayonnaise
1	clove garlic, finely chopped
½	tsp. hot pepper sauce*
1	cup dry seasoned bread crumbs
1	tsp. salt
4	large firm tomatoes, cut into ½-inch-thick slices
	Thinly sliced basil (optional)

Such as Tabasco®.

• Blend Hellmann's® or Best Foods® Light Mayonnaise, garlic and hot pepper sauce in medium bowl; set aside.

• Combine bread crumbs with salt in shallow dish. Brush tomatoes with mayonnaise mixture, then dip in bread crumb mixture.

• Grill tomatoes, 8 minutes or until golden brown. Serve, if desired, with thinly sliced basil.

One-Dish Meals

pasta caponata with pork

MAKES:
4 servings

PREP TIME:
20 minutes

COOK TIME:
25 minutes

Nutrition Information per serving

Calories: 480

Calories From Fat: 110

Total Fat: 12g

Saturated Fat: 2g

Trans Fat: 0g

Cholesterol: 90mg

Sodium: 750mg

Total Carbohydrates: 57g

Dietary Fiber: 15g

Sugars: 25g

Protein: 39g

Vitamin A: 20%

Vitamin C: 25%

Calcium: 10%

Iron: 30%

4	tsp. olive oil, divided
1¼	lbs. pork tenderloin, cut into bite-size pieces
1	medium eggplant, cut into 1-inch pieces
1	large onion, cut into 1-inch pieces
2	stalks celery, sliced
2	Tbsp. golden raisins, chopped (optional)
2	Tbsp. balsamic vinegar
1	jar Bertolli® Vineyard Premium Collections Portobello Mushroom with Merlot Sauce
12	oz. whole wheat linguine, cooked and drained

• Heat 1 teaspoon olive oil in 12-inch nonstick skillet over medium-high heat and cook half of the pork, stirring occasionally, 4 minutes or until done. Remove pork and set aside. Repeat with additional 1 teaspoon olive oil and remaining pork.

• Heat remaining 2 teaspoons olive oil in same skillet and cook eggplant, onion and celery, stirring occasionally, 15 minutes until browned and eggplant is very soft. Stir in raisins, if desired, and vinegar and cook, stirring frequently, 2 minutes. Add Bertolli® Vineyard Premium Collections Portobello Mushroom with Merlot Sauce and bring to a boil over high heat. Reduce heat to medium and cook, stirring occasionally, 3 minutes. Stir in pork and heat through. Serve over hot linguine.

asian salmon salad

MAKES:
4 servings

PREP TIME:
15 minutes

COOK TIME:
12 minutes

Nutrition Information per serving

Calories: 450

Calories From Fat: 170

Total Fat: 19g

Saturated Fat: 2.5g

Trans Fat: 0g

Cholesterol: 60mg

Sodium: 710mg

Total Carbohydrates: 39g

Dietary Fiber: 9g

Sugars: 12g

Protein: 35g

Vitamin A: 40%

Vitamin C: 50%

Calcium: 15%

Iron: 25%

1	medium orange
1	lb. salmon fillet, cut into 4 strips
½	cup Wish-Bone® Light Italian Dressing, divided
3	Tbsp. Skippy® Creamy Peanut Butter
1	tsp. finely grated fresh ginger OR ¼ tsp. ground ginger
8	cups baby spinach leaves
1	small red onion, thinly sliced
1	cup shelled and cooked edamame
⅓	cup sliced almonds, toasted
4	whole wheat dinner rolls

• Preheat oven to 400°F. From the orange, grate enough peel to measure 2 teaspoons; set aside. Peel and section orange; reserve. Arrange salmon in 8-inch glass baking dish; set aside.

• Combine ¼ cup Wish-Bone® Light Italian Dressing, Skippy® Creamy Peanut Butter, orange peel and ginger in small bowl. Evenly spread dressing mixture on salmon. Bake 12 minutes or until salmon flakes with a fork.

• Meanwhile, arrange spinach and onion on serving platter. Top with orange and edamame, then arrange salmon and almonds. Just before serving, drizzle with remaining ¼ cup Dressing and serve with whole wheat dinner rolls.

eggplant "lasagna"

MAKES: 4 servings

COOK TIME: 50 minutes

PREP TIME: 25 minutes

STAND TIME: 15 minutes

Nutrition Information per serving

Calories: 550

Calories From Fat: 240

Total Fat: 27g

Saturated Fat: 11g

Trans Fat: 0g

Cholesterol: 105mg

Sodium: 1,010mg

Total Carbohydrates: 48g

Dietary Fiber: 11g

Sugars: 18g

Protein: 31g

Vitamin A: 40%

Vitamin C: 100%

Calcium: 60%

Iron: 10%

2	Tbsp. olive oil, divided		1	container (16 oz.) part-skim ricotta cheese
1	medium eggplant, cut lengthwise into 9 slices		1	egg, slightly beaten
1	cup canned, rinsed and drained chickpeas		1	clove garlic, chopped
2	large portobello mushrooms, halved and cut into ½-inch-thick slices		2	cups Ragu® Chunky Mama's Special Garden Pasta Sauce, divided
1	large red bell pepper, sliced		1	cup shredded part-skim mozzarella cheese (about 4 oz.), divided
1	medium onion, sliced		2	Tbsp. grated Parmesan cheese

- Preheat oven to 400°F. Brush 2 baking sheets with 2 teaspoons olive oil. Arrange eggplant on baking sheets. Brush with 2 teaspoons olive oil. Bake 20 minutes or until golden; set aside.

- Meanwhile, process chickpeas in food processor until ground; set aside. Heat remaining 2 teaspoons olive oil in 12-inch nonstick skillet over medium-high heat and cook mushrooms, red bell pepper and onion, stirring occasionally, 12 minutes or until vegetables are tender.

- Combine ricotta cheese, beans, egg and garlic in medium bowl; set aside.

- Spread ½ cup Ragu® Chunky Mama's Special Garden Pasta Sauce in 8-inch glass baking dish sprayed with nonstick cooking spray. Arrange 3 slices eggplant on Pasta Sauce, then spread with half of the ricotta cheese mixture. Top with half of the mushroom mixture, then ½ cup Sauce. Sprinkle with ½ cup mozzarella cheese. Top with 3 slices eggplant, remaining ricotta cheese mixture, remaining mushroom mixture, then remaining eggplant. Evenly top with remaining Sauce. Cover with aluminum foil and bake 30 minutes or until bubbling. Remove foil and sprinkle with remaining ½ cup mozzarella and Parmesan cheese. Bake 10 minutes or until cheese is melted.

- Let stand 15 minutes before serving.

vegged-out chili bowls

MAKES:
6 servings

PREP TIME:
10 minutes

COOK TIME:
20 minutes

Nutrition Information per serving

Calories: 490

Calories From Fat: 90

Total Fat: 11g

Saturated Fat: 1g

Trans Fat: 0g

Cholesterol: 40mg

Sodium: 1,230mg

Total Carbohydrates: 66g

Dietary Fiber: 16g

Sugars: 9g

Protein: 38g

Vitamin A: 180%

Vitamin C: 35%

Calcium: 10%

Iron: 30%

1	Tbsp. olive oil
1	medium onion, chopped
1¼	lbs. ground turkey or ground beef
1	jar (1 lb. 10 oz.) Ragu® Old World Style® Pasta Sauce
2	pkg. (16 oz. ea.) frozen mixed vegetables, thawed
1	can (15 oz.) red kidney beans, rinsed and drained
2	Tbsp. chili powder
6	(10-in.) burrito-size spinach, whole wheat or tomato tortillas*
	Shredded Cheddar cheese (optional)
	Low-fat sour cream (optional)

Or, serve over hot cooked rice instead of tortilla bowls.

• Heat olive oil in 5-quart saucepot over medium-high heat; cook onion, stirring occasionally, 3 minutes. Stir in ground turkey and brown. Stir in Ragu® Old World Style® Pasta Sauce, vegetables, beans and chili powder. Bring to a boil over high heat. Reduce heat to low and simmer, stirring occasionally, 10 minutes or until vegetables are tender.

• Meanwhile, gently press 1 tortilla to form a bowl shape in 4-cup microwave-safe bowl. Microwave on HIGH 1½ minutes. Let cool 1 minute. Gently lift out and arrange on serving plate. Repeat with remaining tortillas.

• To serve, spoon chili into tortilla bowls. Garnish, if desired, with shredded Cheddar cheese and low-fat sour cream.

TIP: This chili is all about the veggies so feel free to add any leftovers you have in the fridge.

Not your typical chili...this veggie-packed recipe is served in a homemade tortilla bowl!

peanut chicken curry

MAKES:
4 servings

PREP TIME:
10 minutes

COOK TIME:
15 minutes

Nutrition Information per serving

Calories: 530

Calories From Fat: 150

Total Fat: 17g

Saturated Fat: 4g

Trans Fat: 0g

Cholesterol: 70mg

Sodium: 350mg

Total Carbohydrates: 52g

Dietary Fiber: 8g

Sugars: 10g

Protein: 41g

Vitamin A: 140%

Vitamin C: 90%

Calcium: 10%

Iron: 15%

1	lb. boneless, skinless chicken breasts, cut into 1-inch pieces
	Salt and pepper (optional)
2	Tbsp. I Can't Believe It's Not Butter!® Light Spread
1	cup chopped red bell pepper
1	carrot, chopped
1	cup frozen peas
1	small onion, chopped
1	Tbsp. curry powder
1	clove garlic, chopped
1	container (6 oz.) nonfat plain yogurt
½	cup Skippy® Natural Super Chunk® Peanut Butter Spread
¼	cup water
2	cups cooked white or brown rice
	Lime wedges (optional)

• Season chicken, if desired, with salt and pepper. Melt I Can't Believe It's Not Butter!® Light Spread in 12-inch nonstick skillet over medium-high heat and cook chicken, stirring occasionally, 4 minutes or until chicken is thoroughly cooked; remove and set aside.

• Cook red bell pepper, carrot, peas and onion in same skillet over medium heat, stirring occasionally, 4 minutes or until tender. Stir in curry, garlic and chicken and heat through. Stir in yogurt, Skippy® Natural Super Chunk® Peanut Butter Spread and water until combined and heated through.

• Serve with hot cooked rice and if desired, lime wedges.

farfalle with tuna, lemon & spinach

MAKES:
2 servings

PREP TIME:
20 minutes

COOK TIME:
8 minutes

Nutrition Information per serving

Calories: 480

Calories From Fat: 135

Total Fat: 15g

Saturated Fat: 4g

Trans Fat: 0.5g

Cholesterol: 45mg

Sodium: 890mg

Total Carbohydrates: 54g

Dietary Fiber: 13g

Sugars: 4g

Protein: 37g

Vitamin A: 120%

Vitamin C: 60%

Calcium: 35%

Iron: 40%

3	Tbsp. Promise® Light Spread
1	medium onion, chopped
1/8	tsp. red pepper flakes
4	cloves garlic, finely chopped
1	pkg. (10 oz.) baby spinach leaves
1	can (6 oz.) light tuna packed in water, undrained
8	oz. whole wheat farfalle pasta, cooked according to pkg. directions (reserve ½ cup cooking water)
¼	cup chopped fresh basil leaves
	Grated lemon peel and juice of 1 lemon*
¼	cup grated Parmesan cheese

Use less, if desired.

• Melt Promise® Light Spread in 6-quart saucepot over medium-high heat and cook onion and red pepper flakes, stirring occasionally, 3 minutes or until onion is tender. Add garlic and cook 30 seconds. Add spinach and cook, stirring occasionally, 3 minutes or just until wilted. Stir in tuna. Add pasta, reserved cooking water, basil, lemon peel and lemon juice; heat through. Remove from heat, then stir in cheese.

savory breaded turkey cutlets with stuffing salsa

MAKES:
2 servings

PREP TIME:
15 minutes

COOK TIME:
20 minutes

Nutrition Information per serving

Calories: 470

Calories From Fat: 80

Total Fat: 9g

Saturated Fat: 1.5g

Trans Fat: 0g

Cholesterol: 45mg

Sodium: 520mg

Total Carbohydrates: 59g

Dietary Fiber: 10g

Sugars: 19g

Protein: 39g

Vitamin A: 920%

Vitamin C: 80%

Calcium: 15%

Iron: 25%

4	thin turkey cutlets (about 8 oz.)
1	egg white, slightly beaten
6	whole grain seeded crackers, crumbled (about ⅓ cup)
2	Tbsp. Promise® Buttery Light Spread, divided
1	cup finely chopped carrots (about 2 medium)
½	cup finely chopped celery (about 1 rib)
½	cup finely chopped onion
½	cup finely chopped cremini or white mushrooms (about 4)
1	clove garlic, finely chopped
¼	cup fat-free reduced-sodium chicken broth
1	cup baby spinach leaves, chopped
¼	to ½ tsp. finely chopped fresh rosemary OR ⅛ tsp. dried rosemary, crushed
⅛	tsp. ground black pepper
2	large sweet potatoes, baked

• Dip turkey into egg white, then evenly coat with cracker crumbs. Melt 1 tablespoon Promise® Buttery Light Spread in 12-inch nonstick skillet over medium heat and cook turkey, turning once, 8 minutes or until turkey is thoroughly cooked. Remove turkey and keep warm.

• Melt remaining 1 tablespoon Spread in same skillet and cook carrots, celery, onion and mushrooms, stirring occasionally, 5 minutes or until tender. Stir in garlic and cook 30 seconds. Add remaining ingredients. Cook, stirring occasionally, 2 minutes or until spinach is wilted. Serve turkey with Stuffing Salsa and baked sweet potatoes.

spicy southwest chicken salad

MAKES:
4 servings

PREP TIME:
15 minutes

COOK TIME:
10 minutes

Nutrition Information per serving

Calories: 450

Calories From Fat: 120

Total Fat: 13g

Saturated Fat: 2g

Trans Fat: 0g

Cholesterol: 65mg

Sodium: 890mg

Total Carbohydrates: 50g

Dietary Fiber: 13g

Sugars: 16g

Protein: 36g

Vitamin A: 170%

Vitamin C: 70%

Calcium: 15%

Iron: 20%

½	cup Wish-Bone® Light Italian Dressing, divided
¼	tsp. ground chipotle chile pepper
1	lb. boneless, skinless chicken breasts
1	small onion, cut into ½-inch-thick slices
8	cups spring salad mix
1	can (about 15 oz.) black beans, rinsed and drained
1	medium mango, cut into bite-size pieces
1	medium avocado, cut into bite-size pieces
4	whole wheat dinner rolls

• Combine ¼ cup Wish-Bone® Light Italian Dressing with chipotle chile pepper in small bowl. Brush chicken and onion with dressing mixture.

• Grill or broil chicken and onion, turning once, 10 minutes or until chicken is thoroughly cooked and onion is tender; thinly slice chicken.

• Arrange spring salad mix on serving platter. Top with beans, mango, avocado, onion and chicken. Just before serving, drizzle with remaining ¼ cup Dressing and serve with whole wheat dinner rolls.

tuscan
salmon salad

MAKES:
4 servings

PREP TIME:
15 minutes

COOK TIME:
12 minutes

Nutrition Information per serving

Calories: 480
Calories From Fat: 160
Total Fat: 18g
Saturated Fat: 2g
Trans Fat: 0g
Cholesterol: 60mg
Sodium: 880mg
Total Carbohydrates: 47g
Dietary Fiber: 11g
Sugars: 11g
Protein: 35g
Vitamin A: 40%
Vitamin C: 45%
Calcium: 15%
Iron: 30%

1	medium orange
1	lb. salmon fillet, cut into 4 strips
½	cup Wish-Bone® Light Balsamic Vinaigrette Dressing
8	cups baby spinach leaves
1	small red onion, thinly sliced
1	can (16 oz.) cannellini or white kidney beans, rinsed and drained
⅓	cup toasted pine nuts
4	whole wheat dinner rolls

• Preheat oven to 400°F. From the orange, grate enough peel to measure 2 teaspoons; set aside. Peel and section orange; reserve. Arrange salmon in 8-inch glass baking dish.

• Combine Wish-Bone® Light Balsamic Vinaigrette Dressing with orange peel in small bowl. Evenly brush salmon with 4 tablespoons dressing mixture. Bake 12 minutes or until salmon flakes with a fork.

• Meanwhile, arrange spinach and onion on serving platter. Top with orange and beans, then arrange salmon and pine nuts. Just before serving, drizzle with remaining dressing mixture and serve with whole wheat dinner rolls.

Also terrific with Wish-Bone® Light Italian Dressing.

mushroom, onion & pepper smothered burgers

MAKES:
4 servings

PREP TIME:
15 minutes

COOK TIME:
20 minutes

Nutrition Information per serving with ground beef

Calories: 450
Calories From Fat: 110
Total Fat: 12g
Saturated Fat: 4g
Trans Fat: 0g
Cholesterol: 70mg
Sodium: 620mg
Total Carbohydrates: 49g
Dietary Fiber: 7g
Sugars: 12g
Protein: 35g
Vitamin A: 220%
Vitamin C: 190%
Calcium: 15%
Iron: 35%

2	Tbsp. I Can't Believe It's Not Butter!® Light Spread, divided
1	container (8 oz.) sliced mushrooms
2	medium green, red and/or yellow bell peppers, sliced
1	medium onion, thinly sliced
1	lb. lean ground beef or turkey, shaped into 4 patties
4	whole grain Kaiser rolls or hamburger buns, split and toasted
8	cups romaine lettuce, shredded
2	cups diced tomato
2	cups sliced cucumber
4	Tbsp. Wish-Bone® Light Italian Dressing

• Melt 1 tablespoon I Can't Believe It's Not Butter!® Light Spread in 12-inch nonstick skillet over medium-high heat and cook mushrooms, stirring frequently, 5 minutes or until golden; remove mushrooms from skillet and keep warm.

• Melt remaining 1 tablespoon I Can't Believe It's Not Butter!® Light Spread in same skillet over medium heat and cook bell peppers with onion, stirring frequently, 10 minutes or until very tender. Add to mushrooms and keep warm.

• Cook burgers in same skillet over medium-high heat, turning once, 5 minutes or until burgers are thoroughly cooked. Serve on rolls, then top with mushrooms, bell peppers and onion. In a bowl, combine lettuce, tomato and cucumber. Toss with Wish-Bone® Light Italian Dressing. Serve alongside burgers.

chicken chipotle stew

MAKES:
6 servings

PREP TIME:
15 minutes

COOK TIME:
55 minutes

Nutrition Information per serving

Calories: 450
Calories From Fat: 110
Total Fat: 12g
Saturated Fat: 2.5g
Trans Fat: 0g
Cholesterol: 130mg
Sodium: 420mg
Total Carbohydrates: 37g
Dietary Fiber: 6g
Sugars: 8g
Protein: 4g
Vitamin A: 140%
Vitamin C: 220%
Calcium: 8%
Iron: 15%

1 cup water
2 dried chipotle chilies
1 Tbsp. Knorr® Chicken flavor Bouillon
2 tsp. garlic powder
2½ lbs. chicken, cut into serving pieces (skin removed)
Salt and ground black pepper (optional)
2 Tbsp. vegetable oil

2 medium onions, thinly sliced
2 large carrots, sliced
2 medium zucchini, halved lengthwise and sliced
3 medium green or red bell peppers, cut into strips
3 cups cooked brown rice
Finely chopped fresh oregano leaves (optional)

• Process water, chilies, Knorr® Chicken flavor Bouillon and garlic powder in blender or food processor; set aside.

• Season chicken, if desired, with salt and ground black pepper. Heat oil in 12-inch skillet over medium-high heat and brown chicken, turning occasionally, about 15 minutes. Remove chicken and drippings and set aside.

• Cook onions, carrots, zucchini and green bell peppers in same skillet over medium-high heat, stirring occasionally, 5 minutes or until vegetables are tender.

• Return chicken and drippings to skillet. Pour bouillon mixture over chicken. Simmer, covered, 30 minutes or until chicken is thoroughly cooked. Serve with cooked brown rice and garnish, if desired, with finely chopped fresh oregano leaves.

savory chicken burgers

MAKES: 2 servings

PREP TIME: 12 minutes

COOK TIME: 15 minutes

Nutrition Information per serving

Calories: 450
Calories From Fat: 170
Total Fat: 19g
Saturated Fat: 4g
Trans Fat: 0.5g
Cholesterol: 100mg
Sodium: 610mg
Total Carbohydrates: 46g
Dietary Fiber: 12g
Sugars: 13g
Protein: 30g
Vitamin A: 380%
Vitamin C: 90%
Calcium: 15%
Iron: 25%

2	Tbsp. Promise® Buttery Light Spread, divided
1	cup thinly sliced red onion
4	cremini or white mushrooms, finely chopped (about 1 cup)
1	clove garlic, finely chopped
1	cup firmly packed baby spinach or arugula

½	lb. ground chicken
1	cup finely shredded carrots, chopped
2	green onions, finely chopped
2	100-calorie whole wheat sandwich thins
4	cups romaine lettuce, shredded
1	medium tomato, diced
1	cup sliced cucumbers
3	Tbsp. Wish-Bone® Light Italian Dressing

- Melt 1 tablespoon Promise® Buttery Light Spread in 10-inch nonstick skillet over medium-high heat and cook red onion and mushrooms, stirring occasionally, 4 minutes or until almost tender. Stir in garlic and cook, stirring occasionally, 1 minute or until vegetables are tender. Stir in spinach and cook 1 minute or until wilted. Season, if desired, with fresh black pepper. Remove vegetables from skillet. Reserve half of the vegetable mixture in medium bowl and keep warm.

- Combine ground chicken, carrots, green onions and remaining half of the slightly cooled vegetables in medium bowl; shape into 2 patties.

- Melt remaining 1 tablespoon Spread in same skillet over medium heat and cook burgers, turning once, 8 minutes or until chicken is thoroughly cooked. Arrange burgers on sandwich thins, then top with reserved vegetables.

- In a bowl, combine lettuce, tomato and cucumbers. Toss with Wish-Bone® Light Italian Dressing. Serve alongside Chicken Burgers.

TIP: Substitute ground turkey for ground chicken and prepare as above.

summer panzanella salad

MAKES:
4 servings

PREP TIME:
15 minutes

Nutrition Information per serving

Calories: 520

Calories From Fat: 170

Total Fat: 19g

Saturated Fat: 4.5g

Trans Fat: 0g

Cholesterol: 105mg

Sodium: 750mg

Total Carbohydrates: 37g

Dietary Fiber: 6g

Sugars: 11g

Protein: 47g

Vitamin A: 45%

Vitamin C: 45%

Calcium: 20%

Iron: 25%

3	Tbsp. olive oil
3	Tbsp. red wine vinegar
1	lb. cut-up cooked chicken breasts (about 3 cups)
8	oz. whole grain Italian bread, cut into bite-size pieces
5	cups quartered cherry tomatoes
2	cups coarsely chopped arugula or baby spinach
½	cup chopped part-skim mozzarella cheese (about 2 oz.)
⅓	cup chopped roasted red peppers
¼	cup chopped fresh basil leaves, plus additional for garnish (optional)
¼	tsp. salt

• In large bowl, combine olive oil with vinegar. Add remaining ingredients and toss well. Garnish, if desired, with basil.

fajita chicken salad

MAKES: 4 servings
COOK TIME: 20 minutes
PREP TIME: 20 minutes
MARINATE TIME: 3 hours

Nutrition Information per serving

Calories: 450
Calories From Fat: 100
Total Fat: 11g
Saturated Fat: 2.5g
Trans Fat: 0g
Cholesterol: 65mg
Sodium: 790mg
Total Carbohydrates: 52g
Dietary Fiber: 7g
Sugars: 9g
Protein: 34g
Vitamin A: 150%
Vitamin C: 310%
Calcium: 15%
Iron: 25%

1	cup Wish-Bone® Italian Dressing, divided, plus additional as desired
1	lb. boneless, skinless chicken breasts
2	large red, green or yellow bell peppers, quartered
1	large onion, quartered
4	(6-in.) fajita-size flour tortillas
6	cups torn romaine lettuce leaves
1	medium lime, cut into wedges (optional)

• Pour ¼ cup Wish-Bone® Italian Dressing over chicken in large, resealable plastic bag; turn to coat. Pour ¼ cup Dressing over red bell peppers and onion in another large, resealable plastic bag. Close bags and marinate in refrigerator up to 3 hours.

• Remove chicken and vegetables from marinades, discarding marinades. Grill or broil chicken and vegetables, turning once and brushing frequently with remaining ½ cup Dressing, 12 minutes or until chicken is thoroughly cooked and vegetables are crisp-tender. Lightly grill tortillas, turning once and brushing with additional Dressing, if desired. Tear tortillas into bite-size pieces.

• To serve, thinly slice chicken and vegetables. Arrange lettuce on serving platter, top with chicken, vegetables and tortillas. Serve, if desired, with lime and additional Dressing.

hidden veggie meatballs

MAKES:
4 servings

PREP TIME:
20 minutes

COOK TIME:
20 minutes

Nutrition Information per serving

Calories: 540

Calories From Fat: 120

Total Fat: 13g

Saturated Fat: 3g

Trans Fat: 0.5g

Cholesterol: 115mg

Sodium: 1,240mg

Total Carbohydrates: 71g

Dietary Fiber: 12g

Sugars: 16g

Protein: 37g

Vitamin A: 60%

Vitamin C: 15%

Calcium: 10%

Iron: 70%

1	lb. lean ground beef
½	cup Italian seasoned dry bread crumbs
½	cup finely grated carrot
½	cup finely grated zucchini
1	egg
1	jar (1 lb. 10 oz.) Ragu® Robusto!® Pasta Sauce
8	oz. whole wheat spaghetti, cooked and drained

• Combine ground beef, bread crumbs, carrot, zucchini and egg in medium bowl; shape into 12 meatballs.

• Bring Ragu® Robusto!® Pasta Sauce to a boil in 3-quart saucepan over medium-high heat. Gently stir in uncooked meatballs.

• Reduce heat to low and simmer, covered, stirring occasionally, 20 minutes or until meatballs are done. Serve over hot spaghetti.

TIP: Use the small or tapered end of the vegetable to finely grate the veggies.

warm white bean & tuna quesadillas

MAKES:
4 servings

PREP TIME:
15 minutes

COOK TIME:
5 minutes

Nutrition Information per serving

Calories: 500
Calories From Fat: 160
Total Fat: 18g
Saturated Fat: 7g
Trans Fat: 0g
Cholesterol: 60mg
Sodium: 1,430mg
Total Carbohydrates: 44g
Dietary Fiber: 7g
Sugars: 3g
Protein: 38g
Vitamin A: 10%
Vitamin C: 4%
Calcium: 35%
Iron: 25%

1	can (16 oz.) cannellini or white kidney beans, rinsed and drained
2	cans (6 oz. ea.) tuna in spring water, drained and flaked
¼	cup Hellmann's® or Best Foods® Light Mayonnaise
2	tsp. lemon juice
¼	tsp. salt
4	(8-in.) fajita-size flour tortillas
4	slices Sargento® Deli Style Sliced Mozzarella or Provolone Cheese
1	cup baby spinach leaves

• Lightly mash beans in medium bowl. Stir in tuna, Hellmann's® or Best Foods® Light Mayonnaise, lemon juice and salt. Evenly spread tuna salad onto 2 tortillas, then top with Sargento® Deli Style Sliced Mozzarella or Provolone Cheese, spinach and remaining tortillas.

• Cook quesadillas in 10-inch nonstick skillet lightly sprayed with nonstick cooking spray over medium heat, turning once, 5 minutes or until golden and cheese is melted. Cut into wedges.

vegetarian tacos

MAKES:
4 servings

PREP TIME:
10 minutes

COOK TIME:
7 minutes

Nutrition Information per serving

Calories: 500

Calories From Fat: 130

Total Fat: 15g

Saturated Fat: 5g

Trans Fat: 2g

Cholesterol: 15mg

Sodium: 1,060mg

Total Carbohydrates: 72g

Dietary Fiber: 10g

Sugars: 6g

Protein: 20g

Vitamin A: 50%

Vitamin C: 15%

Calcium: 25%

Iron: 15%

2	tsp. I Can't Believe It's Not Butter!® Light Spread
2	cups cooked brown rice
1	pkg. (1 oz.) taco seasoning mix
⅔	cup water
1	can (15 oz.) red kidney beans, rinsed and drained
12	taco shells, heated
1	cup low-fat Cheddar cheese (about 4 oz.)
1	cup shredded romaine lettuce leaves
1	cup chopped tomato
½	cup low-fat sour cream

• Melt I Can't Believe It's Not Butter!® Light Spread in 12-inch nonstick skillet over medium heat and heat rice and taco seasoning mix, stirring frequently, 2 minutes.

• Stir in water and beans and bring to a boil over high heat. Reduce heat to low and simmer, stirring occasionally, 3 minutes or until liquid is absorbed.

• To serve, evenly spoon bean mixture into taco shells. Top with remaining ingredients.

spicy red lentil vegetable stew

MAKES:
4 servings

PREP TIME:
20 minutes

COOK TIME:
40 minutes

Nutrition Information per serving

Calories: 460
Calories From Fat: 75
Total Fat: 8g
Saturated Fat: 2g
Trans Fat: 0g
Cholesterol: 0mg
Sodium: 1,310mg
Total Carbohydrates: 74g
Dietary Fiber: 16g
Sugars: 10g
Protein: 25g
Vitamin A: 220%
Vitamin C: 90%
Calcium: 10%
Iron: 40%

1½	Tbsp. olive oil
2	medium jalapeño peppers, finely chopped
1	tsp. cumin seeds
2	Knorr® Vegetarian Vegetable Bouillon Cubes, dissolved in 3 cups water
1½	cups red lentils, rinsed and drained
1	can (28 oz.) whole peeled tomatoes, undrained and chopped
4	carrots, cut into 1-inch pieces (about 2 cups)
2	medium potatoes, cut into 1-inch pieces (about 3 cups)
1	Tbsp. curry powder
1	Tbsp. lemon juice
½	cup frozen green peas
	Salt and ground black pepper (optional)
1	Tbsp. chopped fresh cilantro
	Hot cooked rice (optional)

• Heat olive oil in 1-quart saucepan over medium heat and cook jalapeños and cumin seeds, stirring occasionally, 2 minutes. Remove from heat and set aside.

• Bring Knorr® Vegetarian Vegetable Bouillon mixture, lentils, tomatoes with juice, carrots, potatoes, curry powder and lemon juice to a boil in 4-quart saucepot over high heat. Reduce heat to low and simmer, stirring occasionally, 30 minutes or until vegetables are tender. Stir in jalapeño mixture and peas. Simmer, stirring occasionally, 5 minutes. Season, if desired, with salt and ground black pepper. Sprinkle with cilantro and serve, if desired, with hot cooked rice.

black
bean wraps

MAKES:
4 servings

PREP TIME:
15 minutes

COOK TIME:
1 minute

Nutrition Information per serving

Calories: 470
Calories From Fat: 180
Total Fat: 20g
Saturated Fat: 3.5g
Trans Fat: 0g
Cholesterol: 15mg
Sodium: 1,040mg
Total Carbohydrates: 49g
Dietary Fiber: 13g
Sugars: 4g
Protein: 23g
Vitamin A: 45%
Vitamin C: 30%
Calcium: 25%
Iron: 25%

1	can (about 15 oz.) black beans, rinsed and drained
¼	cup Hellmann's® or Best Foods® Light Mayonnaise
½	tsp. garlic powder
4	burrito-size whole wheat tortillas, warmed
1½	cups low-fat Cheddar cheese (about 6 oz.)
2	cups shredded romaine lettuce leaves
1	cup chopped tomatoes
1	medium avocado, sliced

• Mash beans with fork in medium microwave-safe bowl. Stir in Hellmann's® or Best Foods® Light Mayonnaise and garlic powder. Microwave on HIGH, stirring once, 1 minute or until heated through.

• On tortillas, evenly spread bean mixture down centers, then layer on remaining ingredients; roll up and enjoy.

TIP: Add 1 tablespoon lime juice and/or 1 teaspoon hot pepper sauce for additional flavor.

tilapia gremolata

MAKES:
4 servings

PREP TIME:
30 minutes

COOK TIME:
15 minutes

Nutrition Information per serving

Calories: 510

Calories From Fat: 160

Total Fat: 18g

Saturated Fat: 3.5g

Trans Fat: 0g

Cholesterol: 55mg

Sodium: 530mg

Total Carbohydrates: 57g

Dietary Fiber: 7g

Sugars: 7g

Protein: 31g

Vitamin A: 160%

Vitamin C: 70%

Calcium: 8%

Iron: 15%

2	Tbsp. chopped flat-leaf parsley
2	small cloves garlic, chopped, divided
1	tsp. grated lemon peel
2	Tbsp. lemon juice
2	Tbsp. water
1	Knorr® Vegetarian Vegetable Bouillon Cube, crumbled
4	Tbsp. olive oil, divided
4	medium yellow squash and/or zucchini, cut into ribbons
3	medium carrots, peeled and cut into ribbons
1	lb. tilapia fillets
	Ground black pepper (optional)
4	cups hot cooked brown rice

- For gremolata, combine parsley, half of the garlic and lemon peel in small bowl; set aside.

- Microwave lemon juice, water and Knorr® Vegetarian Vegetable Bouillon Cube in small microwave-safe bowl on HIGH 15 seconds. Stir until smooth and set aside.

- Heat 2 tablespoons olive oil in deep 12-inch nonstick skillet over medium-high heat and cook squash and carrots, stirring occasionally, 8 minutes or until tender. Stir in remaining garlic and 2 tablespoons Bouillon mixture and cook 30 seconds. Arrange vegetables on serving platter and keep warm.

- Season tilapia, if desired, with ground black pepper. Heat remaining 2 tablespoons olive oil in same skillet over medium-high heat and cook tilapia, turning once, 5 minutes. Add remaining Bouillon mixture and simmer 1 minute until tilapia flakes with a fork.

- To serve, arrange tilapia on vegetables and top with sauce from skillet. Evenly top with gremolata mixture. Serve with hot rice.

TIP: Use vegetable peeler to easily cut vegetables into ribbons.

hearty beef barley stew

MAKES:
6 servings

PREP TIME:
10 minutes

COOK TIME:
1 hour 45 minutes

Nutrition Information per serving

Calories: 490
Calories From Fat: 190
Total Fat: 21g
Saturated Fat: 7g
Trans Fat: 0g
Cholesterol: 60mg
Sodium: 630mg
Total Carbohydrates: 50g
Dietary Fiber: 10g
Sugars: 6g
Protein: 28g
Vitamin A: 120%
Vitamin C: 20%
Calcium: 4%
Iron: 20%

1	Tbsp. olive oil
1¼	lbs. beef stew meat, cut into 1-inch cubes
2	cups baby carrots
1	pkg. (10 oz.) fresh mushrooms, sliced
1	envelope Lipton® Recipe Secrets® Onion Soup Mix
2	cans (14½ oz. ea.) beef broth
1	can (14½ oz.) diced tomatoes
2	cups water
1¼	cups uncooked pearled barley
1½	cups frozen green peas
	Salt and ground black pepper (optional)

- Heat olive oil in 6-quart saucepot over medium-high heat and brown beef.

- Stir in remaining ingredients except peas.

- Bring to a boil over high heat. Reduce heat to medium-low and simmer, covered, stirring occasionally, 1½ hours or until beef is tender. Stir in peas. Cook 5 minutes or until heated through. Season, if desired, with salt and pepper.

skillet
turkey caesar

MAKES:
4 servings

PREP TIME:
15 minutes

COOK TIME:
12 minutes

Nutrition Information per serving

Calories: 490
Calories From Fat: 190
Total Fat: 21g
Saturated Fat: 4g
Trans Fat: 0g
Cholesterol: 60mg
Sodium: 1,350mg
Total Carbohydrates: 42g
Dietary Fiber: 5g
Sugars: 2g
Protein: 33g
Vitamin A: 50%
Vitamin C: 35%
Calcium: 10%
Iron: 15%

3	Tbsp. olive oil, divided
4	cups cubed French bread (about 7 oz.)
¼	cup grated Parmesan cheese, divided
2	cloves garlic, chopped and divided
⅓	cup Hellmann's® or Best Foods® Light Mayonnaise
¼	cup reduced-sodium chicken broth
1	Tbsp. lemon juice
½	tsp. anchovy paste
2	cups cut-up cooked leftover turkey (8 oz.)
1	can (14 oz.) artichoke hearts, drained and quartered
2	cups shredded romaine lettuce leaves

• For croutons, heat 2 tablespoons olive oil in 12-inch nonstick skillet over medium heat and cook bread, stirring frequently, 2 minutes or until crisp. Stir in ⅛ cup cheese and 1 clove garlic and cook 30 seconds or until croutons are coated. Remove croutons from skillet and set aside.

• Heat remaining 1 tablespoon olive oil in same skillet and cook remaining garlic, stirring frequently, 1 minute. Stir in Hellmann's® or Best Foods® Light Mayonnaise, chicken broth, lemon juice and anchovy paste. Cook, stirring frequently, 2 minutes. Stir in turkey, artichokes and remaining ⅛ cup cheese.

• Stir half of the croutons into skillet. Top with shredded lettuce and remaining croutons.

Snacks

roasted vegetable dip

MAKES:
about 10 servings

PREP TIME:
15 minutes

COOK TIME:
35 minutes

Nutrition Information per 2-Tbsp. serving

Calories: 65

Calories From Fat: 30

Total Fat: 3g

Saturated Fat: 0.5g

Trans Fat: 0g

Cholesterol: 0mg

Sodium: 180mg

Total Carbohydrates: 24g

Dietary Fiber: 5g

Sugars: 5g

Protein: 5g

Vitamin A: 25%

Vitamin C: 100%

Calcium: 4%

Iron: 8%

1 medium zucchini, cut into bite-size pieces

1 medium yellow squash, cut into bite-size pieces

1 medium red bell pepper, cut into bite-size pieces

1 medium red onion, sliced

2 large cloves garlic

1 Tbsp. I Can't Believe It's Not Butter!® Spread

2 tsp. lemon juice

Pinch ground black pepper

4 whole wheat snack-size pita breads, cut into wedges and toasted

• Heat oven to 425°F.

• Toss zucchini, squash, red bell pepper, onion, garlic and I Can't Believe It's Not Butter!® Spread in baking pan. Roast, stirring once, 30 minutes or until very soft and golden.

• Process vegetables, lemon juice and ground black pepper in food processor until smooth. Serve with pita bread wedges or your favorite dippers.

apple streusel muffins

MAKES:
24 mini muffins

PREP TIME:
30 minutes

COOK TIME:
15 minutes

Nutrition Information per serving

Calories: 90
Calories From Fat: 30
Total Fat: 3g
Saturated Fat: 0.5g
Trans Fat: 0g
Cholesterol: 10mg
Sodium: 110mg
Total Carbohydrates: 15g
Dietary Fiber: 0g
Sugars: 7g
Protein: 1g
Vitamin A: 4%
Vitamin C: 0%
Calcium: 2%
Iron: 2%

½	cup water
2	Lipton® Cinnamon Apple Herbal Tea Bags
½	cup raisins
1½	cups PLUS 2 Tbsp. all-purpose flour, divided
¾	cup PLUS 2 Tbsp. sugar, divided
2	tsp. baking powder
½	tsp. salt
⅛	tsp. ground nutmeg (optional)
7	Tbsp. I Can't Believe It's Not Butter!® Spread, divided
1	large egg, beaten

- Preheat oven to 400°F. Spray 2 (12-cup) mini muffin pans with nonstick cooking spray; set aside.

- Bring water to a boil over high heat in 1-quart saucepan. Remove from heat and add Lipton® Cinnamon Apple Herbal Tea Bags and raisins; cover and brew 5 minutes. Remove tea bags and squeeze; cool.

- Combine 1½ cups flour, ¾ cup sugar, baking powder, salt, and if desired, nutmeg in medium bowl. Cut in 6 tablespoons I Can't Believe It's Not Butter!® Spread with pastry blender or 2 knives until mixture is size of small peas. Gently stir in egg and cooled tea mixture just until blended. Spoon batter into prepared pans; set aside.

- Mix remaining 2 tablespoons flour and 2 tablespoons sugar in small bowl. Cut in remaining 1 tablespoon Spread with pastry blender or 2 knives until mixture is size of small peas. Evenly sprinkle onto batter, then pat lightly.

- Bake 15 minutes or until toothpick inserted in center comes out clean. Cool 10 minutes on wire rack; remove from pans and cool completely.

apple
tea latte

MAKES: 1 serving
COOK TIME: 3 minutes
PREP TIME: 5 minutes
BREW TIME: 3 minutes

Nutrition Information per serving

Calories: 130
Calories From Fat: 0
Total Fat: 0g
Saturated Fat: 0g
Trans Fat: 0g
Cholesterol: 0mg
Sodium: 100mg
Total Carbohydrates: 26g
Dietary Fiber: 2g
Sugars: 22g
Protein: 6g
Vitamin A: 10%
Vitamin C: 8%
Calcium: 30%
Iron: 6%

1   cup nonfat soy milk
1   tsp. honey
½   medium apple, chopped
1   Lipton® Black Pearl Black Pyramid Tea Bag

- In 1-quart saucepan, bring soy milk, honey and apple to a boil over high heat. Reduce heat to low and simmer, stirring frequently, 3 minutes.
- Remove saucepan from heat and add Lipton® Black Pearl Black Pyramid Tea Bag and brew 3 minutes. Remove tea bag and squeeze. Strain into mug.

This drinkable snack is filling and provides 300 milligrams of calcium.

bite-you-back
roasted edamame

MAKES:
5 servings

PREP TIME:
10 minutes

COOK TIME:
15 minutes

Nutrition Information per serving

Calories: 100

Calories From Fat: 40

Total Fat: 4g

Saturated Fat: 0g

Trans Fat: 0g

Cholesterol: 0mg

Sodium: 25mg

Total Carbohydrates: 9g

Dietary Fiber: 3g

Sugars: 3g

Protein: 6g

Vitamin A: 6%

Vitamin C: 6%

Calcium: 4%

Iron: 6%

2　tsp. vegetable oil

2　tsp. honey

¼　tsp. wasabi powder*

1　pkg. (10 oz.) shelled edamame, thawed if frozen

　　Kosher salt (optional)

This ingredient can be found in the Asian section of most supermarkets and in Asian specialty markets.

• Preheat oven to 375°F.

• Combine oil, honey and wasabi powder in large bowl; mix well. Add edamame; toss to coat. Spread on baking sheet in single layer.

• Bake 12 to 15 minutes or until golden brown, stirring once. Immediately remove from baking sheet to large bowl; sprinkle generously with salt, if desired. Cool completely before serving. Store in airtight container.

promise® snack mix

MAKES:
4 servings

PREP TIME:
10 minutes

COOK TIME:
10 minutes

Nutrition Information per serving

Calories: 110
Calories From Fat: 30
Total Fat: 3g
Saturated Fat: 0g
Trans Fat: 0g
Cholesterol: 0mg
Sodium: 40mg
Total Carbohydrates: 22g
Dietary Fiber: 2g
Sugars: 0g
Protein: 2g
Vitamin A: 6%
Vitamin C: 0%
Calcium: 0%
Iron: 4%

2	Tbsp. Promise® Buttery Light Spread, melted
½	tsp. ground black pepper
1	cup spoon-size shredded wheat
½	cup unsalted mini pretzels
¼	cup raisins

- Preheat oven to 375°F.
- In medium bowl, combine Promise® Buttery Light Spread, pepper and shredded wheat.
- On jelly-roll pan, evenly spread shredded wheat mixture. Bake 10 minutes; cool slightly. Stir in pretzels and raisins. Cool completely.

wild
wedges

MAKES:
4 servings

PREP TIME:
10 minutes

COOK TIME:
6 minutes

Nutrition Information per serving

Calories: 110

Calories From Fat: 30

Total Fat: 3g

Saturated Fat: 1g

Trans Fat: 0g

Cholesterol: 10mg

Sodium: 270mg

Total Carbohydrates: 13g

Dietary Fiber: 1g

Sugars: 1g

Protein: 8g

Vitamin A: 2%

Vitamin C: 2%

Calcium: 8%

Iron: 6%

2   (8-inch) fat-free flour tortillas

     Nonstick cooking spray

⅓   cup shredded reduced-fat Cheddar cheese

⅓   cup chopped cooked chicken or turkey

1   green onion, thinly sliced

2   Tbsp. mild thick and chunky salsa

• Heat large nonstick skillet over medium heat.

• Spray side of 1 tortilla with nonstick cooking spray; place, sprayed side down, in skillet. Top with cheese, chicken, green onion and salsa. Place remaining tortilla over mixture; spray with cooking spray.

• Cook 2 to 3 minutes per side or until golden brown and cheese is melted. Cut into 8 wedges.

VARIATION: For bean quesadillas, omit the chicken and spread ⅓ cup canned fat-free refried beans over one of the tortillas.

strawberry mango popsicles

MAKES:
4 servings

PREP TIME:
10 minutes

FREEZE TIME:
3 hours

Nutrition Information per serving

Calories: 70

Calories From Fat: 10

Total Fat: 1.5g

Saturated Fat: 0.5g

Trans Fat: 0g

Cholesterol: 0mg

Sodium: 50mg

Total Carbohydrates: 13g

Dietary Fiber: 2g

Sugars: 10g

Protein: 3g

Vitamin A: 15%

Vitamin C: 45%

Calcium: 15%

Iron: 4%

1   can Slim-Fast® 3-2-1 Strawberries 'N Cream Shake

1   cup chopped mango

• On tray, arrange 4 (5-oz.) wax-coated paper cups. Pour Slim-Fast® 3-2-1 Strawberries 'N Cream Shake evenly into cups. Evenly add mango into each cup.

• Freeze 1 hour. Arrange plastic spoon or popsicle stick in center of each cup. Freeze 2 hours or until firm. To serve, peel off paper cups.

peppy snack mix

MAKES:
6 servings

PREP TIME:
10 minutes

COOK TIME:
20 minutes

Nutrition Information per serving

Calories: 100
Calories From Fat: 30
Total Fat: 3g
Saturated Fat: 0g
Trans Fat: 0g
Cholesterol: 0mg
Sodium: 100mg
Total Carbohydrates: 18g
Dietary Fiber: 2g
Sugars: 3g
Protein: 2g
Vitamin A: 6%
Vitamin C: 0%
Calcium: 0%
Iron: 4%

3   (3-inch) plain rice cakes, broken into bite-size pieces
1½ cups bite-size frosted shredded wheat cereal
¾   cup pretzel sticks, halved
3   Tbsp. I Can't Believe It's Not Butter!® Light Spread, melted
2   tsp. reduced-sodium Worcestershire sauce
¾   tsp. chili powder
⅛   to ¼ tsp. ground red pepper

• Preheat oven to 300°F. Combine rice cake pieces, cereal and pretzels in 13×9-inch baking pan. Combine I Can't Believe It's Not Butter!® Light Spread, Worcestershire sauce, chili powder and pepper in small bowl. Drizzle over cereal mixture; toss to combine. Bake 20 minutes, stirring after 10 minutes.

trail mix truffles

MAKES:
8 servings

PREP TIME:
15 minutes

CHILL TIME:
20 minutes

Nutrition Information per serving

Calories: 140
Calories From Fat: 32
Total Fat: 3.5g
Saturated Fat: 1.5g
Trans Fat: 0g
Cholesterol: 0mg
Sodium: 85mg
Total Carbohydrates: 25g
Dietary Fiber: 2g
Sugars: 13g
Protein: 2g
Vitamin A: 4%
Vitamin C: 0%
Calcium: 0%
Iron: 4%

⅓	cup dried apples
¼	cup dried apricots
¼	cup apple butter
2	Tbsp. golden raisins
1	Tbsp. reduced-fat Skippy® peanut butter
½	cup reduced-fat granola
¼	cup graham cracker crumbs, divided
¼	cup mini chocolate chips
1	Tbsp. water

• Blend apples, apricots, apple butter, raisins and peanut butter in food processor until smooth. Stir in granola, 1 tablespoon graham cracker crumbs, chocolate chips and water. Place remaining crumbs in bowl. Shape mixture into 16 balls; roll in remaining crumbs. Cover; refrigerate until ready to serve.

fruit kabobs with raspberry yogurt dip

MAKES:
6 servings

PREP TIME:
15 minutes

Nutrition Information per serving

Calories: 110
Calories From Fat: 0
Total Fat: 0g
Saturated Fat: 0g
Trans Fat: 0g
Cholesterol: 0mg
Sodium: 35mg
Total Carbohydrates: 27g
Dietary Fiber: 2g
Sugars: 22g
Protein: 2g
Vitamin A: 35%
Vitamin C: 100%
Calcium: 4%
Iron: 2%

½   cup plain fat-free yogurt
¼   cup no-sugar-added raspberry fruit spread
1   pt. fresh strawberries
2   cups cubed honeydew melon (1-inch cubes)
2   cups cubed cantaloupe (1-inch cubes)
1   can (8 oz.) pineapple chunks in juice, drained

- For dip, combine yogurt and fruit spread in small bowl until well blended.
- Thread fruit alternately onto 6 (12-inch) wooden skewers. Serve with dip.

129
SNACKS

banana & chocolate chip pops

MAKES:
4 servings

PREP TIME:
12 minutes

FREEZE TIME:
2 hours

Nutrition Information per serving

Calories: 100

Calories From Fat: 20

Total Fat: 2g

Saturated Fat: 1.5g

Trans Fat: 0g

Cholesterol: 0mg

Sodium: 30mg

Total Carbohydrates: 17g

Dietary Fiber: 1g

Sugars: 8g

Protein: 3g

Vitamin A: 3%

Vitamin C: 4%

Calcium: 6%

Iron: 0%

1   small ripe banana

1   carton (8 ounces) banana fat-free yogurt

⅛   tsp. ground nutmeg

2   Tbsp. mini chocolate chips

- Slice banana; place in food processor with yogurt and nutmeg. Process until smooth. Transfer to small bowl; stir in chips.

- Spoon banana mixture into 4 plastic popsicle molds. Place tops on molds; set in provided stand. Set on level surface in freezer; freeze 2 hours or until firm. To unmold, briefly run warm water over popsicle molds until each pop loosens.

rosemary-scented nut mix

MAKES:
32 servings

PREP TIME:
10 minutes

COOK TIME:
15 minutes

Nutrition Information per serving

Calories: 100

Calories From Fat: 90

Total Fat: 10g

Saturated Fat: 1.5g

Trans Fat: 0g

Cholesterol: 0mg

Sodium: 35mg

Total Carbohydrates: 2g

Dietary Fiber: 1g

Sugars: 1g

Protein: 1g

Vitamin A: 0%

Vitamin C: 0%

Calcium: 2%

Iron: 2%

2	Tbsp. unsalted butter
2	cups pecan halves
1	cup unsalted macadamia nuts
1	cup walnuts
1	tsp. dried rosemary
½	tsp. salt
¼	tsp. red pepper flakes

• Preheat oven to 300°F. Melt butter in large saucepan over low heat. Add pecans, macadamia nuts and walnuts; mix well. Add rosemary, salt and red pepper flakes; cook and stir about 1 minute.

• Spread mixture onto ungreased nonstick baking sheet. Bake 15 minutes, stirring occasionally. Cool completely on baking sheet on wire rack.

cinnamon caramel corn

MAKES:
4 servings

PREP TIME:
10 minutes

COOK TIME:
14 minutes

Nutrition Information per serving

Calories: 130

Calories From Fat: 40

Total Fat: 4.5g

Saturated Fat: 2.5g

Trans Fat: 0g

Cholesterol: 10mg

Sodium: 0mg

Total Carbohydrates: 21g

Dietary Fiber: 2g

Sugars: 9g

Protein: 2g

Vitamin A: 2%

Vitamin C: 0%

Calcium: 0%

Iron: 4%

8 cups air-popped popcorn (about ⅓ cup kernels)

2 Tbsp. honey

4 tsp. butter

¼ tsp. ground cinnamon

• Preheat oven to 350°F. Spray jelly-roll pan with nonstick cooking spray. Place popcorn in large bowl.

• Combine honey, butter and cinnamon in small saucepan; cook and stir over low heat until butter is melted and mixture is smooth. Immediately pour over popcorn; toss to coat evenly. Pour onto prepared pan.

• Bake 12 to 14 minutes or until coating is golden brown and appears crackled, stirring twice.

• Cool popcorn on pan. (As popcorn cools, coating becomes crisp. If not crisp enough, or if popcorn softens upon standing, return to oven and heat 5 to 8 minutes.) Store in airtight container.

mediterranean vegetable bruschetta

MAKES:
8 servings

PREP TIME:
15 minutes

COOK TIME:
10 minutes

Nutrition Information per serving

Calories: 110

Calories From Fat: 30

Total Fat: 3g

Saturated Fat: 0.5g

Trans Fat: 0g

Cholesterol: 0mg

Sodium: 290mg

Total Carbohydrates: 19g

Dietary Fiber: 1g

Sugars: 2g

Protein: 4g

Vitamin A: 8%

Vitamin C: 20%

Calcium: 2%

Iron: 6%

3	Tbsp. Promise® Buttery Light Spread, divided
1½	tsp. garlic powder
1	loaf (16-inch) seeded whole wheat baguette, cut into ½-inch slices
1	small onion, finely chopped
1	large zucchini, diced
1	medium tomato, diced
¼	tsp. salt
2	Tbsp. grated Parmesan cheese
2	Tbsp. loosely packed fresh basil leaves, thinly sliced

• Preheat oven to 350°F. Microwave 2 tablespoons Promise® Buttery Light Spread with garlic powder in small microwave-safe bowl or glass measure on HIGH 20 seconds or until melted. Evenly brush onto one side of each bread slice. Arrange bread slices on baking sheet; bake 7 minutes or until toasted; set aside.

• Melt remaining 1 tablespoon Spread in 10-inch nonstick skillet over medium-high heat and cook onion and zucchini, stirring occasionally, 6 minutes or until tender. Stir in tomato and salt. Cook, stirring occasionally, 3 minutes or until tomatoes are tender. Remove from heat and stir in cheese and basil.

• To serve, evenly top each bread slice with 1 tablespoon vegetable mixture.

creamy artichoke bruschetta

MAKES:
10 servings

PREP TIME:
15 minutes

COOK TIME:
1 minute

Nutrition Information per serving

Calories: 100

Calories From Fat: 40

Total Fat: 4g

Saturated Fat: 0.5g

Trans Fat: 0g

Cholesterol: 0mg

Sodium: 250mg

Total Carbohydrates: 14g

Dietary Fiber: 1g

Sugars: 1g

Protein: 3g

Vitamin A: 0%

Vitamin C: 10%

Calcium: 4%

Iron: 4%

1	jar (6 oz.) marinated artichoke hearts, drained and chopped
¼	cup Hellmann's® or Best Foods® Light Mayonnaise
¼	cup finely chopped drained sun-dried tomatoes packed in oil
1	Tbsp. grated Parmesan cheese
1	loaf Italian or French bread (about 15 inches long), cut into ½-inch slices and toasted

- Combine all ingredients except bread in small bowl. Evenly spread artichoke mixture on toasted bread. Broil 1 minute or until golden. Serve immediately.

fruity green tea smoothie

MAKES:
2 (8-oz.) servings

PREP TIME:
10 minutes

CHILL TIME:
15 minutes

Nutrition Information per serving

Calories: 80

Calories From Fat: 0

Total Fat: 0g

Saturated Fat: 0g

Trans Fat: 0g

Cholesterol: 0mg

Sodium: 5mg

Total Carbohydrates: 18g

Dietary Fiber: 2g

Sugars: 11g

Protein: 1g

Vitamin A: 0%

Vitamin C: 8%

Calcium: 0%

Iron: 0%

1	cup boiling water
4	Lipton® Green Tea with Mandarin Orange Flavor Pyramid Tea Bags
2	tsp. sugar
1	medium ripe banana
½	cup ice cubes (about 3 to 4)

* In teapot, pour boiling water over Lipton® Green Tea with Mandarin Orange Flavor Pyramid Tea Bags; cover and brew 1½ minutes. Remove tea bags and squeeze. Stir in sugar and chill. In blender, process tea, banana and ice cubes until blended.

buffalo chicken bites

MAKES:
12 servings

PREP TIME:
20 minutes

COOK TIME:
8 minutes

Nutrition Information per serving

Calories: 80

Calories From Fat: 15

Total Fat: 1.5g

Saturated Fat: 0g

Trans Fat: 0g

Cholesterol: 20mg

Sodium: 190mg

Total Carbohydrates: 7g

Dietary Fiber: 2g

Sugars: 2g

Protein: 10g

Vitamin A: 10%

Vitamin C: 20%

Calcium: 2%

Iron: 4%

2	Tbsp. Promise® Buttery Light Spread, divided
1	lb. boneless, skinless chicken breasts, lightly pounded ¼-inch thick (about 2 breasts)
2	Tbsp. cayenne pepper sauce
12	ribs celery, sliced into 2-inch pieces (36 pieces)
36	cherry tomatoes
½	cup Wish-Bone® Fat Free! Chunky Blue Cheese Dressing

• In 12-inch nonstick skillet, melt ½ tablespoon Promise® Buttery Light Spread over medium heat and cook chicken, turning once, 8 minutes or until chicken is thoroughly cooked; cut into ¾-inch pieces and keep warm.

• Microwave remaining Spread with cayenne pepper sauce in medium microwave-safe bowl on HIGH 15 seconds or until melted; stir until blended. Add chicken; toss to coat.

• On 36 wooden skewers, alternately thread celery, tomatoes and chicken. On serving platter, arrange skewers and serve with Wish-Bone® Fat Free! Chunky Blue Cheese Dressing.

zucchini cake snax

MAKES:
16 servings

PREP TIME:
20 minutes

COOK TIME:
40 minutes

Nutrition Information per square

Calories: 110

Calories From Fat: 35

Total Fat: 3.5g

Saturated Fat: 1g

Trans Fat: 0g

Cholesterol: 25mg

Sodium: 125mg

Total Carbohydrates: 18g

Dietary Fiber: 1g

Sugars: 12g

Protein: 2g

Vitamin A: 6%

Vitamin C: 6%

Calcium: 4%

Iron: 4%

½	cup all-purpose flour
½	cup whole wheat flour
1	tsp. baking powder
¾	tsp. ground cinnamon
¼	tsp. baking soda
¼	tsp. salt
⅓	cup Promise® Buttery Spread
½	cup granulated sugar
⅓	cup firmly packed dark brown sugar
2	eggs
⅓	cup low-fat vanilla yogurt
1½	cups grated zucchini, drained on paper towels (about 2 medium zucchini)

• Preheat oven to 350°F. Line bottom of 9-inch square cake pan* with parchment or waxed paper, then spray with nonstick cooking spray with flour; set aside.

• In medium bowl, combine flours, baking powder, cinnamon, baking soda and salt; set aside.

• In large bowl, with electric mixer, beat Promise® Buttery Spread with sugars until light and fluffy, about 5 minutes. Add eggs, one at a time, beating 1 minute after each addition. Beat in yogurt. Gradually beat in flour mixture, then zucchini, just until blended. Evenly pour into prepared pan.

• Bake 40 minutes or until toothpick inserted in center comes out clean. On wire rack, cool 10 minutes; remove from pan and cool completely. Slice into 16 squares and sprinkle, if desired, with confectioners sugar.

*TO MAKE MINI ZUCCHINI SNAX MUFFINS: Spray mini muffin pans with nonstick cooking spray with flour, then fill ⅔ full with batter. Bake at 350°F for 15 minutes or until toothpick inserted in centers comes out clean. On wire rack, cool 5 minutes; remove from pans and cool completely. Sprinkle, if desired, with confectioners sugar. Makes 3½ dozen.

carrot cake cookies

MAKES: 28 cookies

FREEZE TIME: 2 hours

PREP TIME: 15 minutes

COOK TIME: 8 minutes

Nutrition Information per 2 cookies

Calories: 120

Calories From Fat: 20

Total Fat: 2g

Saturated Fat: 0.5g

Trans Fat: 0g

Cholesterol: 10mg

Sodium: 150mg

Total Carbohydrates: 24g

Dietary Fiber: 1g

Sugars: 14g

Protein: 2g

Vitamin A: 8%

Vitamin C: 0%

Calcium: 2%

Iron: 6%

2	cups quick or old-fashioned oats
1½	cups all-purpose flour
1	tsp. baking soda
1	tsp. salt
4	Tbsp. Promise® Buttery Spread
2	Tbsp. Neufchâtel or ⅓ less fat cream cheese, softened
1¼	cups firmly packed light brown sugar
1	large egg
⅓	cup low-fat vanilla yogurt
1	tsp. vanilla extract
1	cup raisins
½	cup shredded carrot (about 1 large carrot)

Bake just 4 cookies at a time...or the whole batch at once!

- Combine oats, flour, baking soda and salt in medium bowl; set aside.

- Beat Promise® Buttery Spread, cream cheese and brown sugar in large bowl with electric mixer until creamy, about 3 minutes. Beat in egg, yogurt and vanilla until blended. Gradually beat in oat mixture just until blended. Stir in raisins and carrot.

- Turn dough onto waxed paper and form into four 7-inch-long logs. Wrap tightly and freeze 2 hours or until firm.

- Preheat oven to 375°F. For 2 servings, slice off 4 (1-inch rounds) from log, then refreeze remaining dough until ready to bake. Arrange frozen cookie slices on baking sheet. Let stand 10 minutes. Bake 8 minutes or until edges are golden and centers are set. Cool 2 minutes on wire rack; remove from sheet and cool completely.

TIP: Need more cookies? Slice, then bake as many as you need using the above directions.

berry parfait

MAKES:
1 serving

PREP TIME:
5 minutes

COOK TIME:
5 minutes

Nutrition Information per serving

Calories: 120
Calories From Fat: 10
Total Fat: 1g
Saturated Fat: 0g
Trans Fat: 0g
Cholesterol: 0mg
Sodium: 50mg
Total Carbohydrates: 27g
Dietary Fiber: 4g
Sugars: 17g
Protein: 3g
Vitamin A: 6%
Vitamin C: 110%
Calcium: 6%
Iron: 4%

½	cup thinly sliced strawberries
½	cup fresh blueberries
5	sprays I Can't Believe It's Not Butter!® Spray Original
1	Tbsp. orange juice
½	tsp. sugar
¹⁄₁₆	tsp. ground cinnamon
2	Tbsp. nonfat vanilla yogurt
1	Tbsp. low-fat granola cereal

- Preheat 6-inch nonstick skillet over medium-high heat. Add strawberries and blueberries and spray with I Can't Believe It's Not Butter!® Spray Original; toss to coat. Add orange juice, then sprinkle with sugar and cinnamon. Cook, stirring occasionally, 2 minutes or until slightly thickened and just before blueberries burst. Let cool slightly. To serve, top with yogurt and granola.

black pearl hot 'n spicy chocolate tea

MAKES: 2 servings

PREP TIME: 5 minutes

BREW TIME: 1 minute 30 seconds

COOK TIME: 5 minutes

Nutrition Information per serving

Calories: 90

Calories From Fat: 40

Total Fat: 4g

Saturated Fat: 0g

Trans Fat: 0g

Cholesterol: 0mg

Sodium: 65mg

Total Carbohydrates: 19g

Dietary Fiber: 0g

Sugars: 17g

Protein: 4g

Vitamin A: 6%

Vitamin C: 0%

Calcium: 15%

Iron: 2%

1	cup fat-free milk
1	cup water
2	Lipton® Black Pearl Black Pyramid Tea Bags
1	Tbsp. sugar, or to taste
⅛	tsp. ground cinnamon, plus additional as desired
⅛	tsp. ground ginger
⅛	tsp. ground nutmeg
1	tsp. chocolate syrup
	Whipped cream (optional)

• Bring milk and water just to a boil in 2-quart saucepan. Remove from heat and add Lipton® Black Pearl Black Pyramid Tea Bags. Cover and brew 1½ minutes. Remove tea bags and squeeze; stir in remaining ingredients. Serve immediately. Garnish, if desired, with whipped cream and a sprinkle of cinnamon.

Also terrific with Lipton® Cup Size Tea Bags, regular or decaffeinated.

huevos rellenos

MAKES:
6 servings

PREP TIME:
30 minutes

Nutrition Information per serving

Calories: 100
Calories From Fat: 70
Total Fat: 8g
Saturated Fat: 2g
Trans Fat: 0g
Cholesterol: 215mg
Sodium: 240mg
Total Carbohydrates: 1g
Dietary Fiber: 0g
Sugars: 1g
Protein: 6g
Vitamin A: 6%
Vitamin C: 0%
Calcium: 2%
Iron: 4%

6	hard-cooked eggs, halved
3	Tbsp. Hellmann's® or Best Foods® Light Mayonnaise
1	tsp. pickle relish OR finely chopped sweet pickles
1	tsp. Hellmann's® or Best Foods® Dijonnaise ™ Creamy Dijon Mustard
½	tsp. white vinegar
¼	tsp. salt
	Cilantro (optional)
	Paprika (optional)

• Remove egg yolks, reserving egg whites.

• In small bowl, mash egg yolks. Stir in remaining ingredients. Spoon or pipe into egg whites. Chill, if desired. Garnish, if desired, with cilantro and sprinkle with paprika.

Index

Metric Conversion Chart

VOLUME MEASUREMENTS (dry)

1/8 teaspoon = 0.5 mL
1/4 teaspoon = 1 mL
1/2 teaspoon = 2 mL
3/4 teaspoon = 4 mL
1 teaspoon = 5 mL
1 tablespoon = 15 mL
2 tablespoons = 30 mL
1/4 cup = 60 mL
1/3 cup = 75 mL
1/2 cup = 125 mL
2/3 cup = 150 mL
3/4 cup = 175 mL
1 cup = 250 mL
2 cups = 1 pint = 500 mL
3 cups = 750 mL
4 cups = 1 quart = 1 L

VOLUME MEASUREMENTS (fluid)

1 fluid ounce (2 tablespoons) = 30 mL
4 fluid ounces (1/2 cup) = 125 mL
8 fluid ounces (1 cup) = 250 mL
12 fluid ounces (1 1/2 cups) = 375 mL
16 fluid ounces (2 cups) = 500 mL

WEIGHTS (mass)

1/2 ounce = 15 g
1 ounce = 30 g
3 ounces = 90 g
4 ounces = 120 g
8 ounces = 225 g
10 ounces = 285 g
12 ounces = 360 g
16 ounces = 1 pound = 450 g

DIMENSIONS

1/16 inch = 2 mm
1/8 inch = 3 mm
1/4 inch = 6 mm
1/2 inch = 1.5 cm
3/4 inch = 2 cm
1 inch = 2.5 cm

OVEN TEMPERATURES

250°F = 120°C
275°F = 140°C
300°F = 150°C
325°F = 160°C
350°F = 180°C
375°F = 190°C
400°F = 200°C
425°F = 220°C
450°F = 230°C

BAKING PAN SIZES

Utensil	Size in Inches/Quarts	Metric Volume	Size in Centimeters
Baking or Cake Pan (square or rectangular)	8×8×2	2 L	20×20×5
	9×9×2	2.5 L	23×23×5
	12×8×2	3 L	30×20×5
	13×9×2	3.5 L	33×23×5
Loaf Pan	8×4×3	1.5 L	20×10×7
	9×5×3	2 L	23×13×7
Round Layer Cake Pan	8×1½	1.2 L	20×4
	9×1½	1.5 L	23×4
Pie Plate	8×1¼	750 mL	20×3
	9×1¼	1 L	23×3
Baking Dish or Casserole	1 quart	1 L	—
	1½ quarts	1.5 L	—
	2 quarts	2 L	—